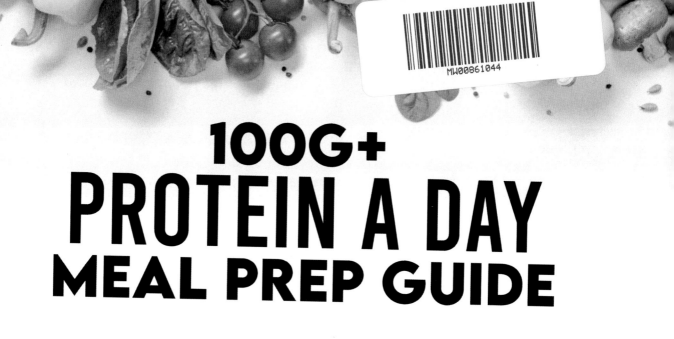

100G+
PROTEIN A DAY
MEAL PREP GUIDE

INTRODUCTION

In today's health-conscious world, a balanced diet that includes an adequate amount of protein is essential for maintaining a healthy and active lifestyle. Protein plays a crucial role in building and repairing tissues, supporting immune function, and providing energy. For those seeking to increase their protein intake, We have curated a collection of 120 delicious recipes that will help you achieve 100g of protein per day goal.

This comprehensive guide includes recipes for breakfast, lunch, dinner, and side dishes, ensuring that you have a diverse range of options to meet your nutritional needs. Whether you're following a high-protein diet for muscle growth, weight management, or simply to improve overall health, these recipes will provide you with the necessary protein intake while offering variety and flavor.

To create these protein-rich recipes, we have focused on incorporating a variety of protein sources that are both nutritious and flavorful. Our selection includes lean meats such as chicken, seafood, and beef, as well as plant-based options like tofu. We have also included a couple of recipes featuring lamb or goat for those who enjoy these protein-rich meats. Eggs and egg whites are utilized in breakfast recipes, adding another excellent source of protein to start your day.

In addition to providing high protein content, we understand the importance of a well-rounded meal. Each recipe is carefully crafted to provide a balanced macronutrient profile, including carbohydrates, fats, and fiber. We have also strived to keep the calorie count of most recipes between 300 to 550 calories, making them suitable for various dietary goals.

With this collection of 120 high-protein recipes, you can easily plan your meals for an extended period without compromising on taste or nutritional value. Each recipe is accompanied by detailed nutrition facts, including the macro breakdown and fiber content. This information allows you to easily track your nutrient intake and make informed choices to align with your health and fitness goals.

Whether you're an avid athlete, a fitness enthusiast, or simply someone looking to incorporate more protein into their diet, these recipes will provide you with the necessary tools to meet your goals. We hope that this compilation of protein-rich recipes will inspire you to explore new flavors and enjoy the benefits of a high-protein diet. Get ready to embark on a culinary journey that combines nutrition and taste, all while fueling your body with the protein it needs to thrive.

100G+
PROTEIN A DAY
MEAL PREP GUIDE

RECIPES AND MEAL PLANS WITH MACROS AND CALORIES

KRUPA AND KRISH

Disclaimer

The cookbook "100g+ Protein a Day Meal Prep Guide: Recipes and Meal Plans with Macros and Calories" is intended to provide general information about meal planning and recipes to achieve a daily protein intake of 100 grams or more. While the cookbook strives to offer accurate nutritional information, readers are advised that individual nutritional needs can vary. It is recommended to consult with a healthcare professional or registered dietitian before making substantial dietary changes. The author and publisher disclaim any liability for the outcomes of following the cookbook's suggestions. Readers are responsible for their own choices and their potential impact on health.

LIST OF HIGH-PROTEIN SOURCES

This recipe collection focuses on incorporating a variety of high-protein sources to ensure a diverse range of flavors and nutritional benefits. Here are some of the key protein sources used in the recipes:

Chicken: Lean cuts of chicken, such as chicken breast, are excellent sources of protein. They can be grilled, roasted, or used in various dishes to add a substantial amount of protein to your meals.

Seafood: Seafood options like salmon, tuna, shrimp, and cod are not only rich in protein but also provide essential omega-3 fatty acids. They can be baked, grilled, or pan-seared to create flavorful and protein-packed meals.

Lean Beef: Opting for lean cuts of beef, such as sirloin or tenderloin, can provide a significant amount of protein while minimizing saturated fats. Sauté, roast, or grill the beef to add protein-rich options to your meals.

Tofu: Tofu is a versatile plant-based protein source that can be used in a variety of dishes. It absorbs flavors well and can be marinated, stir-fried, or grilled to create delicious and protein-packed vegetarian or vegan meals.

Eggs and Egg Whites: Eggs and egg whites are highly nutritious and protein-dense. They can be used in breakfast recipes like omelettes, scrambles, or baked dishes to add protein and create satisfying meals.

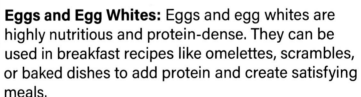

Lamb and Goat: While not as commonly consumed as chicken or beef, lamb and goat are protein-rich options that can add variety to your meals. They can be prepared using various cooking methods such as grilling or slow cooking to enhance their flavors.

HOW TO USE THIS BOOK

This book is designed to provide you with a comprehensive collection of protein-rich recipes that cover all meal times and side dishes. Here's how you can effectively use this book:

Browse and Select Recipes: Start by browsing through the 120 recipes provided in this book. Each recipe specifies the protein content, calories, and macro breakdown, allowing you to choose recipes that align with your dietary goals and preferences.

Plan Your Meals: Once you have selected the recipes you'd like to try, plan your meals for the week. Consider incorporating a variety of protein sources and balancing your meals with carbohydrates, fats, and fiber. The meal plan examples provided in this book can serve as a helpful guide.

Create a Shopping List: Based on your planned meals, create a shopping list to ensure you have all the necessary ingredients. This will help you stay organized and ensure you have everything on hand to prepare your high-protein meals.

Meal Preparation: If you prefer meal prepping, consider dedicating some time to prepare certain components of your meals in advance. For example, you can marinate chicken or chop vegetables ahead of time to streamline the cooking process during busy days.

Enjoy the Recipes: Follow the detailed instructions provided for each recipe to create flavorful and protein-packed meals. Experiment with different flavors, herbs, and spices to customize the recipes to your taste preferences.

Track Your Nutrition: Utilize the nutrition facts provided for each recipe to track your daily protein intake and other macronutrients. This will help you monitor your progress and make adjustments as needed to meet your nutritional goals.

By utilizing this book's recipes, meal planning tips, and high-protein sources, you can create a balanced and protein-rich meal plan that suits your lifestyle and dietary needs. Get ready to explore new flavors, enjoy nutritious meals, and experience the benefits of incorporating over 100g of protein into your daily diet.

TABLE OF CONTENTS

Breakfast Recipes..1
Egg and Spinach Breakfast Scramble................................2
Chicken Sausage and Bell Pepper Omelette.......................3
Savory Quinoa Breakfast Bowl with Chicken and Avocado.....4
Lean Beef Hash with Sweet Potatoes................................5
Tofu Scramble with Vegetables and Avocado......................6
Chickpea Pancakes with Smoked Salmon...........................7
Greek Yogurt Parfait with Mixed Berries and Almonds..........8
High Protein Avocado Toast with Boiled Eggs.....................9
Mediterranean Breakfast Wraps with Grilled Chicken...........10
Baked Beans and Eggs on Whole Grain Toast.....................11
Low Carb Zucchini Frittata with Goat Cheese....................12
Vegan Tofu and Vegetable Frittata.................................13
Egg and Vegetable Breakfast Casserole with Lean Beef........14
Baked Oatmeal with Berries and Cottage Cheese...............15
Smashed Avocado, Chickpea, and Feta on Whole Grain Toast..16
Quinoa and Kale Salad with Boiled Eggs and Avocado..........17
Breakfast Burrito with Scrambled Eggs, Black Beans, and Avocado...18
Protein Pancakes with Greek Yogurt and Fresh Fruits...........19
Three-Minute Egg White Oatmeal....................................20
Vegan Breakfast Sandwich..21

Lunch..22
Grilled Chicken Caesar Salad...23
Teriyaki Salmon with Brown Rice.....................................24
Beef Stir-Fry with Vegetables..25
Tofu and Vegetable Curry...26
Lemon Herb Grilled Chicken with Quinoa..........................27
Shrimp and Avocado Salad..28
Beef and Broccoli Stir-Fry...29
Tofu and Vegetable Stir-Fry..30
Grilled Chicken with Sweet Potato and Green Beans.............31
Chicken Cutlets with Creamy Spinach & Roasted Red Pepper Sauce...32
Spicy Noodles with Lean Beef, Scallions & Bok Choy............33
Mexican Beef and Quinoa Stuffed Sweet Potatoes..............34
Seared Tuna Steak with Avocado and Mango Salsa..............35
Stuffed Chicken Breasts with Tzatziki Sauce......................36
Spicy Thai Basil Tofu Stir Fry..37
Moroccan Lamb Tagine with Chickpeas and Apricots...........38
Mediterranean Shrimp and Artichoke Salad.......................39
Harissa-Roasted Chicken with Quinoa Tabbouleh................40
Sesame Chicken with Green Beans..................................41
Tuna Salad with Mixed Greens.......................................42
Beef and Quinoa Stuffed Bell Peppers.............................43

TABLE OF CONTENTS

Spicy Tofu and Vegetable Noodles...44
Chicken and Black Bean Burrito Bowl..45
Grilled Shrimp Skewers with Quinoa Pilaf...46
Beef and Spinach Salad with Balsamic Vinaigrette............................47
Tofu and Broccoli Stir-Fry...48
Lemon Garlic Grilled Chicken with Quinoa Salad................................49
Grilled Salmon with Roasted Vegetables...50
Tofu and Mushroom Lettuce Wraps...51
Chicken and Vegetable Stir-Fry with Brown Rice...............................52
Spicy Grilled Shrimp with Cauliflower Rice..53
Beef and Quinoa Salad with Balsamic Dressing.................................54
Tofu and Vegetable Curry Soup..55
Grilled Chicken Wrap with Avocado and Spinach..............................56
Salmon and Quinoa Stuffed Zucchini...57
Tofu and Vegetable Skewers with Quinoa..58
Chicken and Brown Rice Soup...59
Shrimp and Quinoa Salad with Lemon Vinaigrette............................60
Lean Beef Burgers...61
Beef and Quinoa Stir-Fry..62

Dinner...63
Chicken Shawarma with Tzatziki Sauce...64
Mexican Shrimp Diablo...65
Butter Chicken with Basmati Rice..66
Beef Tagine with Apricots and Almonds...67
Miso Glazed Salmon...68
Jerk Chicken with Coconut Rice..69
Black Pepper Beef Stir-fry...70
Thai Tofu Green Curry..71
Osso Buco with Gremolata..72
Greek-Style Baked Cod with Lemon and Garlic..................................73
Chicken with Green Sauce...74
Paella with Seafood and Chicken..75
Pho with Beef and Tofu...76
Tuscan Beef and White Bean Stew..77
Chicken with Couscous...78
Miso Salmon...79
Beef and Vegetable Stir-Fry...80
Tofu and Broccoli Stir-Fry..81
Chicken Piccata..82
Grilled Lamb Chops with Mint Chimichurri...83
Szechuan Tofu and Green Beans..84
Grilled Chicken with Peach Salsa...85
Shrimp and Pineapple Fried Rice..86

TABLE OF CONTENTS

Garlic Herb Roasted Chicken..87
Lamb Kofta with Tzatziki..88
Pan-Seared Tofu with Bok Choy and Ginger Soy Sauce...............89
Baked Lemon Herb Salmon..90
Grilled Chicken Caesar Salad...91
Beef and Broccoli Stir Fry...92
Baked Tilapia with Tomato and Basil..93
Chicken and Mushroom Risotto...94
Lemon Garlic Shrimp Pasta...95
Grilled Tofu Kebabs with Peanut Sauce.....................................96
Lemon Herb Roasted Cod with Asparagus...................................97
Balsamic Glazed Chicken and Roasted Vegetables......................98
Beef Stir-Fry with Ginger and Scallions.....................................99
Grilled Lemon Herb Mediterranean Chicken Salad.....................100
Thai Red Curry with Tofu and Vegetables.................................101
Greek-Style Baked Cod with Lemon and Garlic.........................102
Moroccan Chickpea and Vegetable Tagine with Couscous...........103

Side dISHES...104

Balsamic Roasted Brussels Sprouts..105
Garlic Parmesan Roasted Broccoli..106
Steamed Asparagus with Lemon Zest.......................................107
Cilantro Lime Quinoa Salad...108
Greek Salad with Feta and Olives...109
Turmeric Roasted Cauliflower..110
Green Beans Almondine...111
Steamed Bok Choy with Soy Sauce and Ginger.........................112
Sesame Roasted Snap Peas...113
Beetroot and Orange Salad..114
Moroccan Spiced Roasted Carrots..115
Tomato, Cucumber, and Red Onion Salad.................................116
Grilled Zucchini with Lemon Salt..117
Steamed Corn on the Cob with Chili Butter...............................118
Warm Spinach Salad with Roasted Mushrooms.........................119
Caprese Salad with Balsamic Reduction...................................120
Roasted Sweet Potato with Honey and Cinnamon......................121
Asian Slaw with Sesame Ginger Dressing.................................122
Grilled Eggplant with Garlic Yogurt Sauce................................123
Kale Salad with Lemon Vinaigrette...124

7 Days Meal Plan...125

Conclusion..126

BREAKFAST RECIPES

EGG AND SPINACH BREAKFAST SCRAMBLE

Prep time
10 Min

Cook Time
15 Min

Servings
1

Nutrition Information

Calories: 330, Protein: 20g,
Carbs: 3g, Fat: 26g, Fiber: 1g

Ingredients

- 3 large eggs
- 1 cup spinach
- 1 tbsp olive oil
- Salt and pepper to taste

Directions

1. Beat the eggs in a bowl.
2. Heat the olive oil in a pan.
3. Add the spinach and sauté until wilted.
4. Add the beaten eggs, salt, and pepper.
5. Scramble until the eggs are cooked to your desired level.

CHICKEN SAUSAGE AND BELL PEPPER OMELETTE

 Prep time
10 Min

 Cook Time
15 Min

 Servings
1

Nutrition Information

Calories: 470, Protein: 30g,
Carbs: 10g, Fat: 34g, Fiber: 3g

Ingredients

- 2 chicken sausages, chopped
- 3 large eggs
- 1 bell pepper, chopped
- 1 tbsp olive oil
- Salt and pepper to taste

Directions

1. Beat the eggs in a bowl.
2. Heat the olive oil in a pan.
3. Add the chicken sausage and bell pepper. Sauté until the sausage is browned and the pepper is soft.
4. Add the beaten eggs, salt, and pepper.
5. Cook until the eggs are set, then flip and cook the other side.

SAVORY QUINOA BREAKFAST BOWL WITH CHICKEN AND AVOCADO

 Prep time
15 Min

 Cook Time
20 Min

 Servings
1

Nutrition Information

Calories: 520, Protein: 40g,
Carbs: 50g, Fat: 18g, Fiber: 10g

Ingredients

- 1 cup cooked quinoa
- 1 grilled chicken breast, chopped
- 1/2 avocado, sliced
- 1 boiled egg
- Salt and pepper to taste

Directions

1. Prepare the quinoa as per the package instructions.
2. Arrange the quinoa, chicken, avocado, and egg in a bowl.
3. Season with salt and pepper to taste.

LEAN BEEF HASH WITH SWEET POTATOES

 Prep time
15 Min

 Cook Time
30 Min

 Servings
2

Nutrition Information

Calories: 500, Protein: 25g,
Carbs: 40g, Fat: 25g, Fiber: 7g

Ingredients

- 200g lean beef, diced
- 2 sweet potatoes, diced
- 1 onion, diced
- 2 tbsp olive oil
- Salt and pepper to taste

Directions

1. Heat the olive oil in a pan.
2. Add the beef and cook until browned.
3. Add the sweet potatoes and onion. Cook until the potatoes are soft.
4. Season with salt and pepper to taste.

TOFU SCRAMBLE WITH VEGETABLES AND AVOCADO

 Prep time
15 Min

 Cook Time
20 Min

 Servings
1

Nutrition Information

Calories: 400, Protein: 20g,
Carbs: 20g, Fat: 28g, Fiber: 9g

Ingredients

- 1 cup firm tofu, drained and crumbled
- 1 cup mixed vegetables (bell peppers, mushrooms, tomatoes)
- 1/2 avocado, sliced
- 1 tbsp olive oil
- 1/4 tsp turmeric
- Salt and pepper to taste

Directions

1. Heat the olive oil in a pan.
2. Add the vegetables and sauté until softened.
3. Add the crumbled tofu, turmeric, salt, and pepper.
4. Cook for 5-7 mins, stirring occasionally, until the tofu is heated.
5. Serve with the sliced avocado on top.

CHICKPEA PANCAKES WITH SMOKED SALMON

Prep time
15 Min

Cook Time
20

Servings
2

Nutrition Information

Calories: 300, Protein: 21g,
Carbs: 23g, Fat: 12g, Fiber: 5g

Ingredients

- 1/2 cup chickpea flour
- 1/2 cup water
- 1/2 tsp baking powder
- 1/2 tsp salt
- 1 tbsp olive oil
- 100g smoked salmon

Directions

1. Mix the chickpea flour, water, baking powder, and salt until smooth.
2. Heat the olive oil in a pan.
3. To cook the batter, pour half into the pan and cook each side for 2-3 minutes until it turns golden.
4. Repeat with the remaining batter.
5. Serve the pancakes with the smoked salmon.

GREEK YOGURT PARFAIT WITH MIXED BERRIES AND ALMONDS

 Prep time
10 Min

 Cook Time
0 Min

 Servings
1

Nutrition Information

Calories: 320, Protein: 21g,
Carbs: 45g, Fat: 7g, Fiber: 4g

Ingredients

- 1 cup nonfat Greek yogurt
- 1/2 cup mixed berries
- 2 tbsp honey
- 2 tbsp sliced almonds

Directions

1. Layer the Greek yogurt, mixed berries, and honey in a glass.
2. Top with the sliced almonds.

HIGH PROTEIN AVOCADO TOAST WITH BOILED EGGS

 Prep time
15 Min

 Cook Time
10 Min

 Servings
1

Nutrition Information

Calories: 460, Protein: 21g,
Carbs: 34g, Fat: 28g, Fiber: 11g

Ingredients

- 2 slices whole grain bread
- 1 avocado, mashed
- 2 boiled eggs, sliced
- Salt and pepper to taste

Directions

1. Toast the bread.
2. Spread the mashed avocado on the toast.
3. Top with the sliced boiled eggs.
4. Season with salt and pepper to taste.

MEDITERRANEAN BREAKFAST WRAPS WITH GRILLED CHICKEN

Prep time
20 Min

Cook Time
10 Min

Servings
2

Nutrition Information

Calories: 450, Protein: 35g,
Carbs: 40g, Fat: 16g, Fiber: 5g

Ingredients

- 2 whole grain wraps
- 200g chicken breast
- 1/2 cucumber, sliced
- 1 tomato, sliced
- 1/2 cup Greek yogurt
- 1 tbsp olive oil
- Salt and pepper to taste

Directions

1. Warm the olive oil in a grill pan.
2. Season the chicken with salt & pepper, then grill until cooked, about 5-7 minutes on each side.
3. Let the chicken rest for a few minutes, then slice.
4. Assemble the wraps with the sliced chicken, cucumber, tomato, and Greek yogurt.

BAKED BEANS AND EGGS ON WHOLE GRAIN TOAST

 Prep time
5 Min

 Cook Time
15 Min

 Servings
1

Nutrition Information

Calories: 450, Protein: 23g,
Carbs: 55g, Fat: 17g, Fiber: 11g

Ingredients

- 2 slices whole grain bread
- 1 cup canned baked beans
- 2 eggs
- 1 tbsp olive oil
- Salt and pepper to taste

Directions

1. Heat the baked beans in a saucepan over medium heat.
2. Warm the olive oil in another pan and fry the eggs to your liking.
3. Toast the bread.
4. Assemble the baked beans on the toast, then top with the fried eggs.
5. Season with salt and pepper to taste.

LOW CARB ZUCCHINI FRITTATA WITH GOAT CHEESE

 Prep time
15 Min

 Cook Time
20 Min

 Servings
2

Nutrition Information

Calories: 350, Protein: 23g,
Carbs: 10g, Fat: 25g, Fiber: 3g

Ingredients

- 4 eggs
- 2 medium zucchini, sliced
- 1/2 cup goat cheese, crumbled
- 1 tbsp olive oil
- Salt and pepper to taste

Directions

1. Set your oven's heat to 375°F (190°C).
2. In a large-sized oven-safe skillet, heat the olive oil over medium heat. Add the zucchini slices and sauté until tender.
3. In a small-size bowl, whisk the eggs with salt and pepper. Pour the egg mixture over the zucchini into the skillet.
4. Sprinkle the crumbled goat cheese on top.
5. Transfer the skillet to the cooked oven and bake for about 15 mins until the eggs are set.

VEGAN TOFU AND VEGETABLE FRITTATA

Prep time
20 Min

Cook Time
30 Min

Servings
2

Nutrition Information

Calories: 250, Protein: 20g,
Carbs: 20g, Fat: 10g, Fiber: 6g

Ingredients

- 1 cup firm tofu, drained and crumbled
- 2 cups mixed vegetables (bell peppers, onions, tomatoes)
- 1/4 cup nutritional yeast
- 1 tbsp olive oil
- Salt and pepper to taste

Directions

1. Set your oven's temperature to 375°F (190°C).
2. Warm the olive oil in an oven-safe skillet over medium heat. Add the vegetables and sauté until tender. 3
3. combine the tofu, nutritional yeast, salt, and pepper in a blender. Blend until smooth.
4. Pour the tofu mixture over the vegetables in the skillet, stirring to combine.
5. Transfer the skillet to the oven and bake for about 20 minutes or until the tofu is set and lightly browned.
6. Allow to cool for a few minutes before slicing and serving.

EGG AND VEGETABLE BREAKFAST CASSEROLE WITH LEAN BEEF

 Prep time
20 Min

 Cook Time
30 Min

 Servings
4

Nutrition Information

Calories: 350, Protein: 30g,
Carbs: 10g, Fat: 20g, Fiber: 3g

Ingredients

- 8 eggs
- 200g lean beef, diced
- 2 cups mixed vegetables (bell peppers, onions, mushrooms)
- 1 tbsp olive oil
- Salt and pepper to taste

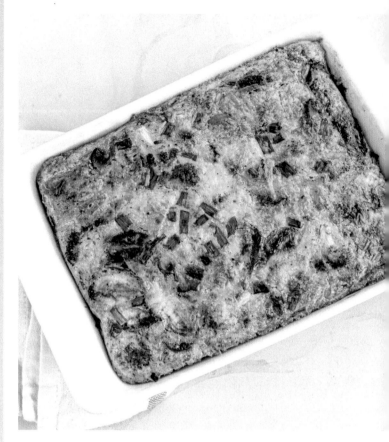

Directions

1. Set your oven's heat to 375°F (190°C).
2. In a nonstick skillet, warm the oil over moderate heat. Add the lean beef and cook until it gets browned. Remove and set aside.
3. In the same skillet, sauté the vegetables until tender.
4. In a large bowl, beat the eggs with salt and pepper.
5. Combine the cooked beef, vegetables, and beaten eggs in a baking dish. Stir to combine.
6. Bake in the oven for 25-30 minutes or until the eggs are set.
7. Allow to cool for a few minutes before slicing and serving.

BAKED OATMEAL WITH BERRIES AND COTTAGE CHEESE

Prep time
10 Min

Cook Time
25 Min

Servings
2

Nutrition Information

Calories: 350, Protein: 20g,
Carbs: 50g, Fat: 8g, Fiber: 7g

Ingredients

- 1 cup rolled oats
- 1 cup mixed berries
- 1 cup cottage cheese
- 2 cups almond milk
- 1 tbsp honey
- 1/2 tsp cinnamon

Directions

1. Adjust your oven's heat to 375°F (190°C).
2. Combine the oats, berries, cottage cheese, almond milk, honey, and cinnamon in a baking dish. Stir until well combined.
3. Prepare in the preheated oven for about 25 mins or until the oats are tender and the liquid has been absorbed.
4. Allow to cool for a few minutes before serving.

SMASHED AVOCADO, CHICKPEA, AND FETA ON WHOLE GRAIN TOAST

 Prep time
10 Min

 Cook Time
0 Min

 Servings
2

Nutrition Information

Calories: 420, Protein: 18g,
Carbs: 50g, Fat: 18g, Fiber: 13g

Ingredients

- 4 slices whole grain bread
- 1 avocado, peeled and pitted
- 1 cup cooked chickpeas
- 1/2 cup feta cheese, crumbled
- 1 tbsp olive oil
- Salt and pepper to taste

Directions

1. In a bowl, combine the avocado and chickpeas. Mash until well combined.
2. Stir in the feta cheese, olive oil, salt, and pepper.
3. Toast the bread.
4. Spread the toasted bread slices evenly over the avocado, chickpea, and feta mixture.
5. Serve immediately.

QUINOA AND KALE SALAD WITH BOILED EGGS AND AVOCADO

 Prep time
15 Min

 Cook Time
20 Min

 Servings
2

Nutrition Information

Calories: 500, Protein: 20g,
Carbs: 55g, Fat: 25g, Fiber: 10g

Ingredients

- 1 cup quinoa
- 2 cups water
- 2 cups chopped kale
- 2 boiled eggs, sliced
- 1 avocado, sliced
- 1 tbsp olive oil
- Lemon juice, salt, and pepper to taste

Directions

1. In a pot, bring the water to a boil. Put in the quinoa, turn the heat down, cover, and simmer for about 15 minutes until the quinoa is tender and the water has been absorbed. Let it cool.
2. Combine the cooked quinoa, chopped kale, sliced boiled eggs, and sliced avocado in a large bowl.
3. To prepare the dish, drizzle olive oil and lemon juice over it. Then, add some salt & pepper to season it. Toss to combine.
4. Serve immediately.

BREAKFAST BURRITO WITH SCRAMBLED EGGS, BLACK BEANS, AND AVOCADO

 Prep time
15 Min

 Cook Time
15 Min

 Servings
2

Nutrition Information

Calories: 550, Protein: 25g,
Carbs: 50g, Fat: 28

Ingredients

- 2 large whole-grain tortillas
- 4 eggs
- 1 cup packed black beans, washed and drained
- 1 avocado, sliced
- 1 tbsp olive oil
- Salt and pepper to taste

Directions

1. In a bowl, beat the eggs. Warm half the olive oil in a skillet and scramble the eggs to your liking. Set aside.
2. In the same skillet, warm the remaining olive oil. Add the black beans and sauté until heated through.
3. You can either use a dry skillet or microwave to warm the tortillas.
4. Assemble the burritos by dividing the scrambled eggs, black beans, and avocado slices between the tortillas. Season with salt and pepper.
5. Roll up the tortillas, tucking in the sides as you go

PROTEIN PANCAKES WITH GREEK YOGURT AND FRESH FRUITS

 Prep time
15 Min

 Cook Time
10 Min

 Servings
2

Nutrition Information

Calories: 350, Protein: 18g,
Carbs: 45g, Fat: 10g, Fiber: 6g

Ingredients

- 1/2 cup oat flour
- 1/2 cup Greek yogurt
- 2 eggs
- 1/2 tsp baking powder
- 1 tbsp honey
- 1/2 cup mixed fresh fruits (like berries or banana slices)

Directions

1. Mix the oat flour, Greek yogurt, eggs, baking powder, and honey until smooth.
2. Heat a nonstick skillet over medium heat. Pour 1/4 of the batter into the skillet for each pancake.
3. Cook for 2-3 minutes on each side until the pancakes are golden brown.
4. Serve the pancakes topped with Greek yogurt and fresh fruits.

THREE-MINUTE EGG WHITE OATMEAL

 Prep time
1 Min

 Cook Time
3 Min

 Servings
1

Nutrition Information

Calories: 250, Protein: 20g,
Carbs: 35g, Fat: 2.5g, Fiber: 5g

Ingredients

- 1/2 cup rolled oats
- 1 cup water or milk of choice
- 3 egg whites (about 1/3 cup)
- Pinch of salt
- 1 tbsp honey or sweetener of choice
- Optional toppings: fresh fruits, nuts, seeds, cinnamon

Directions

1. Combine the rolled oats and water (or milk) in a microwave-safe bowl. Microwave for 2 minutes on high.
2. Generously remove the bowl from the microwave (it will be hot), and stir in the egg whites and salt.
3. Return the bowl to the microwave, and cook for another minute on high or until the oatmeal has thickened to your liking.
4. Stir in the honey or sweetener of choice.
5. Top with your favorite toppings, if desired, and serve immediately.

VEGAN BREAKFAST SANDWICH

Prep time
15 Min

Cook Time
15 Min

Servings
1

Nutrition Information

Calories: 300, Protein: 18g,
Carbs: 30g, Fat: 12g, Fiber: 6g

Ingredients

- 1 whole-grain English muffin
- 1/4 block of firm tofu
- 1/2 cup spinach
- 1 slice of tomato
- 1 tbsp nutritional yeast
- 1/4 tsp turmeric
- 1 tbsp olive oil
- Salt and pepper to taste

Directions

1. To remove any extra moisture, drain and press the tofu. Slice into a rectangle about the size of your English muffin.
2. Warm the olive oil in a skillet over medium heat. Add the tofu and sprinkle with nutritional yeast, turmeric, salt, and pepper. Cook for a few minutes on each side until the tofu is heated through and lightly golden.
3. While the tofu is cooking, toast your English muffin.
4. Assemble your sandwich by layering the cooked tofu, fresh spinach, and tomato slice on the English muffin.
5. Serve immediately.

LUNCH

GRILLED CHICKEN CAESAR SALAD

Prep time
15 Min

Cook Time
15 Min

Servings
2

Nutrition Information

Calories: 350Protein: 42g,
Carbs: 12g, Fat: 18g, Fiber: 5g

Ingredients

- 2 boneless, skinless chicken breasts
- 1 head of romaine lettuce, watered and chopped
- 1/4 cup grated Parmesan cheese
- 1/4 cup Caesar dressing
- Salt and pepper to taste

Directions

1. Preheat the grill to medium-high heat.
2. Season the chicken breasts with salt & pepper.
3. Grill the chicken for 6-8 mins per side until cooked through.
4. Let the chicken rest for a few minutes, then slice it into strips.
5. Combine the romaine lettuce, Parmesan cheese, and Caesar dressing in a large bowl. Toss well to coat.
6. To serve, evenly distribute the salad onto separate plates and add the grilled chicken.
7. Serve immediately.

TERIYAKI SALMON WITH BROWN RICE

 Prep time
10 Min

 Cook Time
20 Min

 Servings
2

Nutrition Information

Calories: 450, Protein: 44g,
Carbs: 48g, Fat: 12g, Fiber: 3g

Ingredients

- 2 salmon fillets
- 1/4 cup teriyaki sauce
- 2 cups cooked brown rice
- 1 cup steamed broccoli florets
- Sesame seeds for garnish

Directions

1. Set the oven's heat to 400°F (200°C).
2. Set the salmon fillets in a baking pan and brush them with teriyaki sauce.
3. Bake the salmon for about 15-20 minutes until cooked through.
4. In a serving bowl, divide the cooked brown rice and steamed broccoli.
5. Place the teriyaki salmon fillets on top.
6. Sprinkle with sesame seeds for garnish.
7. Serve hot.

BEEF STIR-FRY WITH VEGETABLES

Prep time
15 Min

Cook Time
10 Min

Servings
4

Nutrition Information

Calories: 400, Protein: 46g ,
Carbs: 25g , Fat: 14g , Fiber: 6g

Ingredients

- 1 pound beef sirloin, thinly sliced
- 2 tablespoons soy sauce
- 1 tablespoon cornstarch
- 1 tablespoon sesame oil
- 2 cloves garlic, minced
- 1 tablespoon grated fresh ginger
- 2 cups mixed vegetables (like bell peppers, broccoli, and carrots)
- Salt and pepper to taste
- 2 tablespoons vegetable oil

Directions

1. Combine the sliced beef, soy sauce, and cornstarch in a bowl. Let it marinate for 10 minutes.
2. Heat the sesame oil over highly-heat in a large skillet or wok.
3. Add the mashed garlic and grated ginger, and stir-fry for about 1 minute until fragrant.
4. Add the marinated beef and prepare for 2-3 minutes until browned.
5. Add the mixed vegetables and stir-fry for 3-4 minutes until the vegetables are tender-crisp.
6. Season with salt and pepper to taste.
7. Serve hot with steamed rice or noodles.

TOFU AND VEGETABLE CURRY

Prep time
10 Min

Cook Time
20 Min

Servings
4

Nutrition Information

Calories: 320, Protein: 42g
Carbs: 30g , Fat: 10g , Fiber: 8g

Ingredients

- 1 package of firm tofu, cubed
- 1 tablespoon vegetable oil
- 1 onion, diced
- 2 cloves garlic, minced
- 1 tablespoon grated fresh ginger
- 2 tablespoons curry powder
- 1 can (14 oz) coconut milk
- 2 cups mixed vegetables (bell peppers, carrots, and peas)
- Salt and pepper to taste
- Fresh cilantro for garnish
- Cooked rice for serving

Directions

1. In a large-sized pan, heat the vegetable oil over medium heat.
2. Add the diced onion, minced garlic, and grated ginger. Sauté for 2-3 minutes until the onion becomes translucent.
3. Once you've added the curry powder, cook it for a minute to toast the spices.
4. Add the cubed tofu and mixed vegetables to the pan. Stir to coat them with the curry mixture.
5. Pour in the coconut milk and take it to a simmer. Let it cook for 10-15 minutes until the vegetables are tender.
6. Season with salt and pepper to taste.
7. Garnish with fresh cilantro and serve with cooked rice.

LEMON HERB GRILLED CHICKEN WITH QUINOA

 Prep time
10 Min

 Cook Time
20 Min

 Servings
2

Nutrition Information

Calories: 400 , Protein: 45g
Carbs: 40g , Fat: 15g , Fiber: 6g

Ingredients

- 2 boneless, skinless chicken breasts
- Juice of 1 lemon
- Zest of 1 lemon
- 2 cloves garlic, minced
- 1 tablespoon chopped fresh herbs (basil, thyme)
- Salt and pepper to taste
- 1 cup cooked quinoa
- Steamed vegetables for serving

Directions

1. Preheat the grill to medium-high heat.
2. Combine the lemon juice, lemon zest, minced garlic, chopped fresh herbs, salt, and pepper in a small bowl.
3. Set the chicken breasts in a shallow dish and pour the marinade over them. Allow them to marinate for 10 minutes.
4. Grill the chicken breasts for about 6-8 minutes per side until cooked through and nicely charred.
5. Take away the chicken from the grill and rest for a few minutes.
6. Slice the grilled chicken and serve it over cooked quinoa.
7. Serve with steamed vegetables on the side.

SHRIMP AND AVOCADO SALAD

 Prep time
15 Min

 Cook Time
5 Min

 Servings
2

Nutrition Information

Calories: 350, Protein: 42g,
Carbs: 18g, Fat: 20g, Fiber: 9g

Ingredients

- 1/2 pound shrimp, peeled and deveined
- 2 cups mixed salad greens
- 1 avocado, diced
- 1/4 cup cherry tomatoes, halved
- 1/4 cup sliced red onions
- 2 tablespoons lemon juice
- 1 tablespoon olive oil
- Salt and pepper to taste

Directions

1. Heat a skillet over medium-high heat. Add the shrimp and prepare for 2-3 minutes per side until they turn pink and opaque.
2. Combine the mixed salad greens, diced avocado, cherry tomatoes, and sliced red onions in a large-sized bowl.
3. Whisk the lime juice, olive oil, salt & pepper in a small-size bowl o make the dressing.
4. Add the prepared shrimp to the salad and drizzle with the dressing.
5. Toss well to coat all the ingredients.
6. Serve immediately.

BEEF AND BROCCOLI STIR-FRY

Prep time
15 Min

Cook Time
10 Min

Servings
4

Nutrition Information

Calories: 450, Protein: 43g,
Carbs: 20g, Fat: 16g, Fiber: 4g

Ingredients

- 1 pound beef sirloin, thinly sliced
- 3 tablespoons soy sauce
- 2 tablespoons oyster sauce
- 2 tablespoons cornstarch
- 1 tablespoon vegetable oil
- 3 cloves garlic, minced
- 1 tablespoon grated fresh ginger
- 4 cups broccoli florets
- Salt and pepper to taste

Directions

1. Combine the sliced beef, soy sauce, oyster sauce, and cornstarch in a bowl. Allow it to marinate for 10 minutes.
2. Warm the vegetable oil in a large-sized skillet or wok over high heat.
3. Add the mashed garlic and grated ginger, and stir-fry for about 1 minute until fragrant.
4. Place the beef marinated in the skillet and stir-fry it for 2-3 minutes until it turns brown.
5. Add the broccoli florets and stir-fry for 3-4 minutes until the broccoli is tender-crisp.
6. Season with salt and pepper to taste.
7. Serve hot with steamed rice or noodles.

TOFU AND VEGETABLE STIR-FRY

Prep time
15 Min

Cook Time
10 Min

Servings
4

Nutrition Information

Calories: 350, Protein: 42g,
Carbs: 28g, Fat: 11g, Fiber: 7g

Ingredients

- 1 package of firm tofu, cubed
- 2 tablespoons soy sauce
- 1 tablespoon cornstarch
- 1 tablespoon vegetable oil
- 1 onion, sliced
- 2 cloves garlic, minced
- 2 cups mixed vegetables (bell peppers, broccoli, and carrots)
- Salt and pepper to taste

Directions

1. Combine the cubed tofu, soy sauce, and cornstarch in a bowl. Allow it to marinate for 10 minutes.
2. Wam the vegetable oil in a large-sized skillet or wok over medium-high heat.
3. Add the sliced onion and mashed garlic, and stir-fry for 2 minutes until softened.
4. Place the marinated tofu in the skillet, and stir-fry it for 4-5 minutes until it turns golden brown.
5. Add the mixed vegetables and continue stir-frying for another 3-4 minutes until the vegetables are tender-crisp.
6. Season with salt and pepper to taste.
7. Serve hot with steamed rice or noodles.

GRILLED CHICKEN WITH SWEET POTATO AND GREEN BEANS

Prep time
15 Min

Cook Time
25 Min

Servings
2

Nutrition Information

Calories: 400, Protein: 45g,
Carbs: 35g, Fat: 12g, Fiber: 8g

Ingredients

- 2 boneless, skinless chicken breasts
- 2 small sweet potatoes, peeled and diced
- 1 cup green beans, trimmed
- 2 tablespoons olive oil
- 1 teaspoon dried rosemary
- Salt and pepper to taste

Directions

1. Preheat the grill to medium-high heat.
2. To prepare the chicken, sprinkle salt, pepper, and dried rosemary seasoning onto the pieces.
3. Grill the chicken for 6-8 minutes per side until cooked through.
4. Meanwhile, steam the diced sweet potatoes and green beans in a steamer or microwave-safe dish until tender.
5. In a non-stick pan, warm the olive oil over medium heat.
6. Add the steamed sweet potatoes and green beans to the skillet, and sauté for 3-4 minutes until lightly browned.
7. Season with salt and pepper to taste.
8. Serve the grilled chicken with the sautéed sweet potatoes and green beans.

CHICKEN CUTLETS WITH CREAMY SPINACH & ROASTED RED PEPPER SAUCE

 Prep time
15 Min

 Cook Time
20 Min

 Servings
4

Nutrition Information

Calories: 380 Protein: 34g Carbs: 9g Fat: 23g Fiber: 2g

Ingredients

- 4 boneless, skinless chicken breast cutlets
- Salt and pepper, to taste
- 1/2 cup all-purpose flour
- 2 tablespoons olive oil
- 2 cloves garlic, minced
- 4 cups fresh spinach leaves
- 1 cup roasted red peppers, sliced
- 1 cup heavy cream
- 1/4 cup grated Parmesan cheese

Directions

1. Salt and pepper the chicken cutlets on each side. Coat them with flour and shake off any extra.
2. Warm olive oil in a large-sized skillet on medium-high. Cook chicken cutlets for 3–4 minutes per side until golden brown and cooked through. Set aside the chicken.
3. Sauté the minced garlic for 1 minute in the same skillet until fragrant.
4. Wilt fresh spinach in the skillet.
5. Add the sliced roasted red peppers to the pan along with the spinach.
6. Add heavy cream and boil. The sauce should thicken after 3–4 minutes.
7. Melt and mix the Parmesan cheese.
8. Return the chicken cutlets to the skillet and cook for 2-3 minutes, allowing them to heat through and absorb some of the sauce.
9. Serve the chicken cutlets with the creamy spinach and roasted red pepper sauce.

SPICY NOODLES WITH LEAN BEEF, SCALLIONS & BOK CHOY

 Prep time
15 Min

 Cook Time
20 Min

 Servings
4

Nutrition Information

Calories: 460, Protein: 40g,
Carbs: 44g, Fat: 12g, Fiber: 4g

Ingredients

- 8 ounces dried noodles (such as ramen noodles or spaghetti)
- 1 tablespoon vegetable oil
- 1 pound lean beef, thinly sliced
- 4 cloves garlic, mashed
- 2 teaspoons fresh ginger, grated
- 2 tablespoons soy sauce
- 1 tablespoon oyster sauce
- 1 tablespoon hoisin sauce
- 1 tablespoon chili paste or sriracha sauce (adjust to taste)
- 2 cups bok choy, chopped
- 4 scallions, sliced
- Salt and pepper, to taste

Directions

1. Cook the noodles as per the package instructions. Drain and set aside.
2. Warm the vegetable oil over moderate-high heat in a large skillet or wok. Add the sliced beef and cook until browned and cooked through. Remove the beef from the skillet and place aside.
3. In the same skillet, add the mashed garlic and grated ginger. Stir-fry for about 1 minute until fragrant.
4. Add the soy sauce, oyster sauce, hoisin sauce, and chili paste or sriracha sauce to the skillet. Stir to combine.
5. Add the chopped bok choy to the skillet and stir-fry for about 2-3 minutes until it starts to wilt.
6. Return the prepared beef to the skillet and add the cooked noodles. Toss everything together until well coated with the sauce.
7. Add the sliced scallions and season with salt and pepper to taste. Stir-fry for an additional 1-2 minutes.
8. Remove from heat and serve the spicy noodles with lean beef, scallions, and bok choy.

MEXICAN BEEF AND QUINOA STUFFED SWEET POTATOES

 Prep time
10 Min

 Cook Time
60 Min

 Servings
1

Nutrition Information

Calories: 550, Protein: 42g,
Carbs: 60g, Fat: 15g, Fiber: 10g

Ingredients

- 1 large sweet potato
- 150g lean ground beef
- 1/2 cup cooked quinoa
- 1/4 cup corn
- 1/4 cup black beans
- 1/4 cup shredded cheddar cheese
- 1/4 teaspoon chili powder
- Salt to taste

Directions

1. Preheat your oven to 400F. To prepare the sweet potato, poke holes and bake it for approximately 45-50 minutes until it becomes soft.
2. While the potato is baking, cook the beef in a skillet until no pink remains.
3. Stir in the cooked quinoa, corn, black beans, chili powder, and salt.
4. When the sweet potato is done, cut it open and stuff it with the beef and quinoa mixture. Top with shredded cheddar and return to the oven for 10 minutes or until the cheese is melted.

SEARED TUNA STEAK WITH AVOCADO AND MANGO SALSA

Prep time
10 Min

Cook Time
10 Min

Servings
1

Nutrition Information

Calories: 530, Protein: 45g,
Carbs: 30g, Fat: 25g, Fiber: 10g

Ingredients

- 150g fresh tuna steak
- 1/2 ripe mango, diced
- 1/2 ripe avocado, diced
- 1/4 red onion, finely chopped
- Juice of 1 lime
- Salt and pepper to taste

Directions

1. Heat a skillet over high heat. Season the tuna steak with salt & pepper and sear it for 2 minutes on each side for medium-rare.
2. While the tuna is cooking, combine the mango, avocado, red onion, and lime juice to make the salsa. Season with salt and pepper.
3. Serve the seared tuna with the avocado mango salsa on top.

STUFFED CHICKEN BREASTS WITH TZATZIKI SAUCE

 Prep time
15 Min

 Cook Time
30 Min

 Servings
1

Nutrition Information

Calories: 350, Protein: 42g,
Carbs: 10g, Fat: 15g, Fiber: 2g

Ingredients

- 150g skinless chicken breast
- 1/4 cup chopped spinach
- 2 tbsp crumbled feta cheese
- 1/2 cup Greek yogurt
- 1/4 cucumber, grated
- 1 clove garlic, minced
- Juice of 1/2 lemon
- Salt and pepper to taste

Directions

1. Preheat your oven to 375F. Cut a pocket into the chicken breast and stuff it with the chopped spinach and feta cheese. Secure with toothpicks if necessary.
2. Place the chicken on a baking tray and bake for about 25-30 minutes or until the chicken gets fully cooked.
3. Make the tzatziki sauce while the chicken is cooking by combining Greek yogurt, grated cucumber, minced garlic, lemon juice, and salt.
4. Serve the stuffed chicken breast with tzatziki sauce.

SPICY THAI BASIL TOFU STIR FRY

Prep time
15 Min

Cook Time
15 Min

Servings
1

Nutrition Information

Calories: 400, Protein: 42g,
Carbs: 45g, Fat: 10g, Fiber: 5g

Ingredients

- 200g firm tofu, cubed
- 1 cup of fresh basil leaves
- 1 red bell pepper, sliced
- 2 cloves of garlic, minced
- 1 red chili, sliced
- 2 tbsp soy sauce
- 1 tbsp vegetable oil
- Steamed rice to serve

Directions

1. Warm oil in a large-sized skillet over medium-high heat. Add tofu cubes and cook until it gets golden brown on all sides. Remove tofu and set aside.
2. Add garlic, red chili, and bell pepper in the same skillet. Stir-fry for a couple of minutes until the pepper softens.
3. Add the tofu to the skillet, add soy sauce, and stir well. Cook for another 2 minutes.
4. Please turn off the heat, add the basil leaves, and stir until they're wilted.
5. Serve the stir-fry over steamed rice.

MOROCCAN LAMB TAGINE WITH CHICKPEAS AND APRICOTS

 Prep time
20 Min

 Cook Time
60 Min

 Servings
1

Nutrition Information

Calories: 550, Protein: 40g,
Carbs: 45g, Fat: 25g, Fiber: 8g

Ingredients

- 150g lamb shoulder, cut into chunks
- 1/4 cup dried apricots
- 1/2 cup cooked chickpeas
- 1/2 onion, chopped
- 1 clove garlic, minced
- 1/2 teaspoon ground cumin
- 1/2 teaspoon ground cinnamon
- 1/2 teaspoon ground turmeric
- 1 tablespoon olive oil
- Salt to taste

Directions

1. Warm the olive oil in a tagine or heavy-bottomed pot over moderate heat. Set the lamb in the pan and cook until browned on all sides.
2. To soften the onion, cook it with the garlic in the pot.
3. Add the cumin, cinnamon, turmeric, and salt to the pot and stir well. Add the apricots and chickpeas, cover the pot, and reduce the heat to low.
4. Let the tagine simmer for about 1 hour or until the lamb is tender.
5. Serve the tagine with couscous or bread if desired.

MEDITERRANEAN SHRIMP AND ARTICHOKE SALAD

 Prep time
15 Min

 Cook Time
5 Min

 Servings
1

Nutrition Information

Calories: 400, Protein: 40g,
Carbs: 20g, Fat: 20

Ingredients

- 150g cooked shrimp
- 1 cup canned artichoke hearts, drained
- 1/2 cup cherry tomatoes, halved
- 1/4 cup kalamata olives, split and halved
- 2 cups mixed salad greens
- 1 tablespoon olive oil
- Juice of 1/2 lemon
- Salt and pepper to taste

Directions

1. Combine the shrimp, artichoke hearts, cherry tomatoes, and olives in a large bowl.
2. To prepare the salad, gently pour olive oil and lemon juice. Then, add a pinch of salt & pepper for seasoning. Toss well.
3. Serve the salad over mixed greens.

HARISSA-ROASTED CHICKEN WITH QUINOA TABBOULEH

 Prep time
20 Min

 Cook Time
30 Min

 Servings
1

Nutrition Information

Calories: 400, Protein: 42g,
Carbs: 30g, Fat: 12g, Fiber: 6g

Ingredients

- 150g skinless chicken breast
- 1 tablespoon harissa paste
- 1/2 cup cooked quinoa
- 1/2 cup chopped fresh parsley
- 1/4 cup chopped fresh mint
- 1/2 cucumber, diced
- 10 cherry tomatoes, halved
- Juice of 1 lemon
- 1 tablespoon olive oil
- Salt and pepper to taste

Directions

1. Preheat your oven to 375F. Rub the chicken breas
   with the harissa paste, season with salt and
   pepper, and place it on a baking sheet. Roast for
   25-30 minutes or until the chicken is fully cooked
2. While the chicken is roasting, prepare the
   tabbouleh. Combine the cooked quinoa, parsley,
   mint, cucumber, and cherry tomatoes in a bowl.
   Add some lemon juice and olive oil to make a
   delicious dish, season it with salt and pepper, and
   combine it well.
3. Serve the roasted chicken with the quinoa
   tabbouleh.

SESAME CHICKEN WITH GREEN BEANS

Prep time
15 Min

Cook Time
15 Min

Servings
1

Nutrition Information

Calories: 410, Protein: 40g,
Carbs: 20g, Fat: 18g, Fiber: 4g

Ingredients

- 180g skinless chicken breast, cut into bite-sized pieces
- 1 cup green beans, ends trimmed
- 2 tbsp soy sauce
- 1 tbsp sesame oil
- 1 tbsp honey
- 1 tbsp sesame seeds
- 2 cloves garlic, minced
- 1/4 teaspoon crushed red pepper flakes
- Salt to taste
- 1 tablespoon vegetable oil

Directions

1. Mix soy sauce, sesame oil, honey, sesame seeds, garlic, red pepper flakes, and a bit of salt in a bowl.
2. Toss chicken in the basin. Marinate chicken for 10 minutes.
3. Medium-heat vegetable oil in a big skillet. Cook the chicken and marinade for 8-10 minutes.
4. While the chicken cooks, steam the green beans for 4-5 minutes until cooked but crisp.
5. Toss chicken and green beans in a skillet. Heat for another 2-3 minutes.
6. Serve the sesame chicken and green beans with steamed rice if desired.

TUNA SALAD WITH MIXED GREENS

 Prep time
15 Min

 Cook Time
5 Min

 Servings
2

Nutrition Information

Calories: 400, Protein: 44g,
Carbs: 15g, Fat: 18g, Fiber: 6g

Ingredients

- 2 tuna steaks
- 6 cups mixed salad greens
- 1 cup cherry tomatoes, halved
- 1/2 cucumber, sliced
- 1/4 red onion, thinly sliced
- 2 tablespoons olive oil
- 2 tablespoons lemon juice
- Salt and pepper to taste

Directions

1. Add salt with pepper to taste the tuna steaks.
2. Warm a skillet over high heat and sear the tuna steaks for 1-2 minutes per side or until desired doneness.
3. Remove the tuna steaks from the skillet and let them rest for a few minutes before slicing.
4. Combine the mixed salad greens, cherry tomatoes, cucumber, and red onion in a large bowl.
5. Whisk the oil, lime juice, salt & pepper in a small-size bowl to make the dressing.
6. To coat the salad, drizzle the dressing over it and toss.
7. To serve, evenly distribute the salad among the plates and add sliced seared tuna. Serve immediately.

BEEF AND QUINOA STUFFED BELL PEPPERS

Prep time
20 Min

Cook Time
40 Min

Servings
4

Nutrition Information

Calories: 380, Protein: 41g,
Carbs: 30g, Fat: 14g, Fiber: 6g

Ingredients

- 4 bell peppers (any color)
- 1 pound lean ground beef
- 1 cup cooked quinoa
- 1/2 onion, diced
- 2 cloves garlic, minced
- 1 cup diced tomatoes
- 1/2 cup shredded mozzarella cheese
- 1 teaspoon dried oregano
- 1 teaspoon dried basil
- Salt and pepper to taste

Directions

1. Set the oven's heat to 375°F (190°C).
2. Remove bell pepper seeds and membranes.
3. Brown ground beef in a large skillet over moderate heat. Remove fat.
4. Cook the diced onion and mashed garlic in the skillet for 2-3 minutes until transparent.
5. Add cooked quinoa, diced tomatoes, dried oregano, basil, salt, and pepper. Cook another 2-3 minutes to blend flavors.
6. Stuff bell peppers with beef-quinoa mixture.
7. Place the stuffed bell peppers in a foil-covered baking dish.
8. Bake for 30 minutes. Remove the wrap and top each bell pepper with shredded mozzarella cheese.
9. Prepare for 10 minutes until the cheese melts and bubbles.
10. Then serve the filled bell peppers.

SPICY TOFU AND VEGETABLE NOODLES

 Prep time
15 Min

 Cook Time
15 Min

 Servings
2

Nutrition Information

Calories: 360, Protein: 43g,
Carbs: 32g, Fat: 10g, Fiber: 7g

Ingredients

- 8 oz firm tofu, drained and cubed
- 4 oz rice noodles
- 1 red bell pepper, thinly sliced
- 1 carrot, julienned
- 1/2 zucchini, thinly sliced
- 2 green onions, sliced
- 2 tablespoons soy sauce
- 1 tablespoon sriracha sauce (adjust to taste)
- 1 tablespoon sesame oil
- 1 tablespoon vegetable oil
- 2 cloves garlic, minced
- 1 teaspoon grated ginger
- Sesame seeds for garnish
- Fresh cilantro for garnish

Directions

1. Prepare the rice noodles as per the package guidlines. Drain and set aside.
2. Mix the soy sauce, sriracha sauce, sesame oil, chopped garlic, and grated ginger in a small-sized bowl.
3. Warm the vegetable oil in a large-sized skillet or wok over medium-high heat.
4. Add the tofu cubes and prepare until golden brown and crispy on all sides. Remove from the skillet and set aside.
5. Add the sliced bell pepper, julienned carrot, and zucchini to the same skillet. Stir-fry for 3-4 minutes until the vegetables are tender-crisp.
6. Add the cooked rice noodles, cooked tofu, and the sauce mixture to the skillet. Toss everything together until well combined and heated through.
7. Once removed from the heat, garnish the dish with sliced green onions, sesame seeds, and fresh cilantro.
8. Serve hot, and enjoy!

CHICKEN AND BLACK BEAN BURRITO BOWL

 Prep time
15 Min

 Cook Time
25 Min

 Servings
4

Nutrition Information

Calories: 420, Protein: 44g,
Carbs: 38g, Fat: 15g, Fiber: 9g

Ingredients

- 1 pound boneless, skinless chicken breasts, diced
- 1 cup cooked brown rice
- 1 cup pack black beans, washed and drained
- 1 red bell pepper, diced
- 1/2 red onion, diced
- 1 cup corn kernels
- 1 teaspoon chili powder
- 1/2 teaspoon cumin
- 1/2 teaspoon paprika
- 1/4 teaspoon garlic powder
- Salt and pepper to taste
- 1 tablespoon olive oil
- Fresh cilantro for garnish
- Lime wedges for serving

Directions

1. Combine the chili powder, cumin, paprika, garlic powder, salt, and pepper in a small bowl.
2. Season the diced chicken breasts with the spice mixture, ensuring they are evenly coated.
3. Warm the olive oil in a large-sized skillet over medium-high heat.
4. Add the seasoned chicken to the skillet until browned and cooked, about 6-8 minutes. Remove from the skillet and set aside.
5. Add the diced red bell pepper and red onion to the same skillet. Prepare for 3-4 minutes until the vegetables are tender.
6. Add the cooked brown rice, black beans, and corn kernels to the skillet. Stir everything together and cook for 2-3 minutes to heat through.
7. Return the cooked chicken to the skillet and toss everything together to combine.
8. After removing from heat, add a fresh cilantro garnish. To serve, place the chicken and black bean mixture in bowls and provide lime wedges on the side.

GRILLED SHRIMP SKEWERS WITH QUINOA PILAF

 Prep time
20 Min

 Cook Time
15 Min

 Servings
2

Nutrition Information

Calories: 380, Protein: 46g,
Carbs: 35g, Fat: 12g, Fiber: 6g

Ingredients

For the Shrimp Skewers:
- 12 large shrimp, peeled and deveined
- 2 tablespoons olive oil
- 1 tablespoon lemon juice
- 1 clove garlic, minced
- 1 teaspoon paprika
- 1/2 teaspoon dried oregano
- Salt and pepper to taste

For the Quinoa Pilaf:
- 1 cup cooked quinoa
- 1/4 cup diced red bell pepper
- 1/4 cup diced yellow bell pepper
- 1/4 cup diced zucchini
- 1/4 cup diced red onion
- 1 tablespoon chopped fresh parsley
- 1 tablespoon lemon juice
- 1 tablespoon olive oil
- Salt and pepper to taste

Directions

1. In a bowl, combine the oil, lime juice, minced garlic, paprika, dried oregano, salt & pepper. Stir well to create a marinade.
2. Put the shrimp peeled and deveined into the marinade and mix it well to ensure it is coated. Le it marinate for about 10 minutes.
3. Preheat the grill to medium-high heat.
4. Thread the marinated shrimp onto skewers.
5. Grill the shrimp skewers for 2-3 minutes per side until they are pink and opaque.
6. In the meantime, prepare the quinoa pilaf. In a separate bowl, combine the prepared quinoa, diced red bell pepper, diced yellow bell pepper, diced zucchini, diced red onion, chopped fresh parsley, lemon juice, olive oil, salt, and pepper. Toss everything together until well combined.
7. Put the grilled shrimp skewers on top of the quinoa pilaf to serve.
8. Enjoy!

BEEF AND SPINACH SALAD WITH BALSAMIC VINAIGRETTE

 Prep time
15 Min

 Cook Time
10 Min

 Servings
2

Nutrition Information

Calories: 420, Protein: 42g,
Carbs: 15g, Fat: 20g, Fiber: 5g

Ingredients

For the Salad:
- 8 ounces lean beef steak, thinly sliced
- 4 cups fresh spinach leaves
- 1 cup cherry tomatoes, halved
- 1/2 red onion, thinly sliced
- 1/4 cup crumbled feta cheese
- 2 tablespoons chopped walnuts

For the Balsamic Vinaigrette:
- 2 tablespoons balsamic vinegar
- 1 tablespoon olive oil
- 1 teaspoon Dijon mustard
- 1 teaspoon honey
- Salt and pepper to taste

Directions

1. Heat a skillet over medium-high heat. Add the thinly sliced beef and cook for about 3-4 minutes per side until browned and cooked to your desired level of doneness. Remove from heat and let it rest for a few minutes. Then, thinly slice the beef into strips.
2. Combine the fresh spinach leaves, cherry tomatoes, thinly sliced red onion, crumbled feta cheese, and chopped walnuts in a large salad bowl.
3. Whisk the balsamic vinegar, olive oil, Dijon mustard, honey, salt, and pepper in a small-sized bowl until well combined.
4. Drizzle the balsamic vinaigrette over the salad ingredients and toss gently to coat.
5. Divide the salad mixture between two plates.
6. Arrange the sliced beef strips on top of the salad.
7. Serve the beef and spinach salad immediately.

TOFU AND BROCCOLI STIR-FRY

Prep time
10 Min

Cook Time
15 Min

Servings
2

Nutrition Information

Calories: 340, Protein: 41g,
Carbs: 26g, Fat: 10g, Fiber: 7g

Ingredients

- 8 ounces firm tofu, drained and cubed
- 2 cups broccoli florets
- 1 bell pepper, sliced
- 1 carrot, julienned
- 1/2 onion, sliced
- 2 cloves garlic, minced
- 2 tablespoons soy sauce
- 1 tablespoon hoisin sauce
- 1 tablespoon sesame oil
- 1/2 teaspoon ginger powder
- Salt and pepper to taste
- Optional: Sesame seeds for garnish

Directions

1. Medium-high heat sesame oil in a big skillet or wok.
2. Add mashed garlic and chopped onion to the skillet. Sauté until translucent.
3. Cook cubed tofu in the skillet for 5 minutes until lightly browned.
4. Add bell pepper, carrot, and broccoli florets to skillet. Stir-fry until crisp.
5. Mix soy sauce, hoisin sauce, ginger powder, salt, and pepper in a small bowl.
6. Pour sauce over tofu and vegetables in a skillet. Mix well.
7. Stir occasionally for 2 more minutes.
8. If desired, decorate with sesame seeds. Serve the tofu and broccoli stir-fry hot with steamed rice or noodles.

LEMON GARLIC GRILLED CHICKEN WITH QUINOA SALAD

Prep time
15 Min

Cook Time
20 Min

Servings
2

Nutrition Information

Calories: 460, Protein: 45g,
Carbs: 35g,Fat: 14g, Fiber: 7g

Ingredients

For the Lemon Garlic Grilled Chicken:
- 2 boneless, skinless chicken breasts
- 2 cloves garlic, minced
- Zest and juice of 1 lemon
- 1 tablespoon olive oil
- Salt and pepper to taste

For the Quinoa Salad:
- 1 cup cooked quinoa
- 1 cup cherry tomatoes, halved
- 1/2 cucumber, diced
- 1/4 red onion, thinly sliced
- 2 tablespoons chopped fresh parsley
- 2 tablespoons lemon juice
- 1 tablespoon olive oil
- Salt and pepper to taste

Directions

1. Preheat the grill to medium-high heat.
2. Mix the garlic, lemon zest, lime juice, olive oil, salt, and pepper in a bowl.
3. Lemon garlic marinates the chicken breasts in a shallow dish. Marinate chicken for 10 minutes.
4. Grill the chicken breasts on each side for 6-8 minutes until cooked through and 165°F (75°C). Rest a few minutes after grilling. Chicken strips.
5. Cook the quinoa per the package directions, then mix it with the diced cucumber, red onion, chopped parsley, lemon juice, olive oil, salt & pepper. Mix well.
6. Divide the quinoa salad between two plates and top with the sliced grilled chicken.
7. Serve the lemon garlic grilled chicken with quinoa salad immediately.

GRILLED SALMON WITH ROASTED VEGETABLES

Prep time
15 Min

Cook Time
25 Min

Servings
2

Nutrition Information

Calories: 420, Protein: 42g,
Carbs: 20g, Fat: 16g, Fiber: 8g

Ingredients

- 2 salmon fillets (6 ounces each)
- 2 tablespoons olive oil, divided
- 1 teaspoon lemon zest
- 1 tablespoon lemon juice
- 2 cloves garlic, minced
- Salt and pepper to taste
- 1 medium zucchini, sliced
- 1 red bell pepper, sliced
- 1 yellow bell pepper, sliced
- 1 small red onion, sliced
- 1 cup cherry tomatoes
- Fresh dill for garnish

Directions

1. Preheat the grill to medium heat.
2. In a small-sized bowl, combine 1 tablespoon of olive oil, lemon zest, lemon juice, minced garlic, salt, and pepper.
3. Lay the salmon fillets on a plate and brush the lemon garlic mixture over both sides of the salmon. Let it marinate for 10 minutes.
4. Mix the sliced zucchini, red and yellow bell peppers, red onion, and cherry tomatoes in another bowl with 1 tbsp of oil, salt & pepper.
5. Place the marinated salmon fillets and the prepared vegetables on the grill. Cook the salmon for 4-5 minutes per side or until it flakes easily with a fork. Grill the vegetables for 8-10 minutes until tender and slightly charred.
6. Remove the salmon and vegetables from the grill. Let the salmon rest for a few minutes.
7. Serve the grilled salmon alongside the roasted vegetables. Garnish with fresh dill.
8. Enjoy your delicious and healthy meal!

TOFU AND MUSHROOM LETTUCE WRAPS

 Prep time
15 Min

 Cook Time
15 Min

 Servings
2

Nutrition Information

Calories: 380, Protein: 40g,
Carbs: 22g, Fat: 13g, Fiber: 6g

Ingredients

- 1 block firm tofu, drained and pressed
- 2 tablespoons soy sauce
- 1 tablespoon hoisin sauce
- 1 tablespoon rice vinegar
- 1 tablespoon sesame oil
- 2 cloves garlic, minced
- 1 teaspoon grated ginger
- 1 cup sliced mushrooms
- 1/2 cup shredded carrots
- 1/4 cup chopped green onions
- Lettuce leaves for wrapping
- Sesame seeds for garnish

Directions

1. Whisk together soy sauce, hoisin sauce, rice vinegar, sesame oil, minced garlic, and grated ginger to make the sauce in a small bowl.
2. Cut the pressed tofu into small cubes.
3. Heat a non-stick skillet over moderate heat and add the tofu cubes. Prepare for about 5 minutes, stirring occasionally, until the tofu is lightly browned.
4. Add the sliced mushrooms, shredded carrots, and chopped green onions to the skillet. Cook for another 5 mins until the vegetables are tender.
5. Pour the prepared sauce over the tofu and vegetables into the skillet. Stir well to coat everything evenly. Prepare for 2-3 minutes to allow the flavors to meld together.
6. Remove the skillet from heat and let the mixture cool slightly. Take a lettuce leaf and spoon some of the tofu and vegetable mixture onto it. Garnish with sesame seeds.
7. Repeat with the remaining lettuce leaves and filling. Serve the tofu and mushroom lettuce wraps as a light and flavorful meal.

CHICKEN AND VEGETABLE STIR-FRY WITH BROWN RICE

Prep time
15 Min

Cook Time
20 Min

Servings
2

Nutrition Information

Calories: 480, Protein: 44g,
Carbs: 40g, Fat: 10g

Ingredients

- 2 boneless, skinless chicken breasts, thinly sliced
- 2 tablespoons soy sauce
- 1 tablespoon oyster sauce
- 1 tablespoon cornstarch
- 2 tablespoons vegetable oil, divided
- 2 cloves garlic, minced
- 1 teaspoon grated ginger
- 1 red bell pepper, thinly sliced
- 1 yellow bell pepper, thinly sliced
- 1 small broccoli crown, cut into florets
- 1 carrot, julienned
- 1/2 cup snap peas
- 2 cups cooked brown rice
- Sesame seeds for garnish
- Chopped green onions for garnish

Directions

1. In a small-sized bowl, whisk together soy sauce, oyster sauce, and cornstarch to make the sauce. Set aside.
2. First, heat up one tablespoon of vegetable oil in a big skillet or wok on medium-high heat.
3. Add the sliced chicken to the skillet and cook for about 5-6 minutes until it is browned and cooked. Take the chicken out of the skillet and keep it aside.
4. Pour the remaining tbsp of vegetable oil into the skillet you used before. Add the minced garlic and grated ginger. Stir-fry for about 1 minute until fragrant.
5. Add the sliced bell peppers, broccoli florets, julienned carrot, and snap peas to the skillet. Stir-fry for about 5-6 minutes until the vegetables are tender-crisp.
6. After cooking the chicken and vegetables in a skillet, return the chicken to the skillet and pour the sauce over everything. Stir it well to ensure an even coating. Allow it to cook for 2-3 minutes until the sauce thickens. Once done, remove the skillet from the heat.
7. Serve the chicken and vegetable stir-fry over prepared brown rice and garnish with mashed green onions and sesame seeds.
8. Enjoy a flavorful and nutritious meal!

SPICY GRILLED SHRIMP WITH CAULIFLOWER RICE

Prep time
15 Min

Cook Time
10 Min

Servings
24

Nutrition Information

Calories: 320, Protein: 43g,
Carbs: 12g, Fat: 18g, Fiber: 5g

Ingredients

- 12 large shrimp, peeled and deveined
- 2 tablespoons olive oil
- 1 teaspoon paprika
- 1/2 teaspoon cayenne pepper
- 1/2 teaspoon garlic powder
- 1/2 teaspoon salt
- 1/4 teaspoon black pepper
- 2 cups cauliflower rice
- 1 tablespoon butter
- 1 clove garlic, minced
- 1/4 cup diced bell peppers
- 1/4 cup diced onions
- 1/4 cup diced tomatoes
- Fresh cilantro for garnish
- Lime wedges for serving

Directions

1. Preheat the grill to medium-high heat.
2. Combine olive oil, paprika, cayenne pepper, garlic powder, salt, and black pepper in a bowl. Put the shrimp in the bowl and toss them around so the spice mixture covers them evenly.
3. Skewer and grill shrimp. Grill shrimp for 2-3 minutes per side until done and slightly scorched. Set aside after grilling.
4. Melt butter in a skillet. Add minced garlic, diced onions, and bell peppers. Cook for about two to three minutes or until the veggies are soft.
5. Add the cauliflower rice and diced tomatoes to the skillet. Cook for 3-4 minutes until the cauliflower rice is heated through.
6. Divide the cauliflower rice mixture onto plates and top with the grilled shrimp.
7. Garnish with fresh cilantro, then serve with lime wedges on the side.
8. Enjoy the spicy and flavorful grilled shrimp with cauliflower rice!

BEEF AND QUINOA SALAD WITH BALSAMIC DRESSING

 Prep time
15 Min

 Cook Time
20 Min

 Servings
2

Nutrition Information

Calories: 400, Protein: 41g,
Carbs: 30g Fat: 14g, Fiber: 6g

Ingredients

- gredients:
- 8 ounces lean beef steak, thinly sliced
- 1 cup cooked quinoa
- 2 cups mixed salad greens
- 1/2 cup cherry tomatoes, halved
- 1/4 cup sliced red onions
- 1/4 cup crumbled feta cheese
- 2 tablespoons chopped fresh parsley

For the Balsamic Dressing:
- 2 tablespoons balsamic vinegar
- 1 tablespoon olive oil
- 1 teaspoon Dijon mustard
- 1 teaspoon honey
- Salt and pepper to taste

Directions

1. Warm a grill pan or skillet over moderate-high heat. Season the beef steak with salt & pepper. Prepare the steak for 2-3 minutes per side until cooked to your desired level of doneness. Remove from heat and let it rest for a few minutes. Slice the steak into thin strips.
2. Combine the cooked quinoa, mixed salad greens, cherry tomatoes, sliced red onions, crumbled feta cheese, and chopped fresh parsley in a large mixing bowl. Toss to combine.
3. Mix balsamic vinegar, olive oil, Dijon mustard, honey, salt, and pepper in a small-size bowl to make the dressing. Then, add the sliced beef steak to the quinoa salad mixture. To ensure every ingredient is covered, gently mix the salad after pouring the balsamic dressing.
4. Divide the salad into individual serving plates or bowls.
5. Serve the beef and quinoa salad as a delicious and satisfying meal.

TOFU AND VEGETABLE CURRY SOUP

Prep time
15 Min

Cook Time
25 Min

Servings
4

Nutrition Information

Calories: 220, Protein: 42g
Carbs: 28g, Fat: 11g, Fiber: 7g

Ingredients

- 1 tablespoon coconut oil
- 1 onion, diced
- 2 cloves garlic, minced
- 1 tablespoon grated ginger
- 2 tablespoons curry powder
- 1 teaspoon turmeric
- 1 teaspoon cumin
- 1/2 tsp chili powder (to taste)
- 1 can (14 ounces) of coconut milk
- 4 cups vegetable broth
- 1 cup diced carrots
- 1 cup diced bell peppers
- 1 cup diced zucchini
- 1 cup diced mushrooms
- 1 package (14 ounces) of firm tofu, cubed
- Salt and pepper to taste
- Fresh cilantro for garnish
- Lime wedges for serving

Directions

1. Medium-heat coconut oil in a big pot. Dice onion, mince garlic, and grated ginger. Sauté until translucent.
2. Add the spices of curry, turmeric, cumin, and chili powder to the pot. Toss the onion mixture with seasonings. Toasted spices increase flavor.
3. Add coconut milk and vegetable broth. Mix everything by stirring it. Simmer the mixture.
4. Add diced carrots, bell peppers, zucchini, and mushrooms to the pot. Stir soup to distribute vegetables properly. Keep the lid on the saucepan and let it simmer over low heat for fifteen minutes or until the vegetables are soft.
5. Add cubed tofu gently. Salt & pepper to taste. To heat tofu, simmer for 5 more minutes.
6. Serve tofu and vegetable curry soup. Serve with lime wedges and fresh cilantro.
7. Enjoy the comforting and flavorful tofu and vegetable curry soup!

GRILLED CHICKEN WRAP WITH AVOCADO AND SPINACH

 Prep time
15 Min

 Cook Time
20 Min

 Servings
2

Nutrition Information

Calories: 400, Protein: 45g,
Carbs: 35g, Fat: 12g, Fiber: 8g

Ingredients

- 2 boneless, skinless chicken breasts
- 1 tablespoon olive oil
- 1 teaspoon paprika
- 1/2 teaspoon garlic powder
- Salt and pepper to taste
- 2 whole wheat wraps or tortillas
- 1 ripe avocado, sliced
- 1 cup fresh spinach leaves
- 1/4 cup sliced red onions
- 2 tablespoons Greek yogurt or sour cream (optional)

Directions

1. Set the grill or grill pan over moderate-high heat.
2. In a small-sized bowl, combine the olive oil, paprika, garlic powder, salt & pepper to make a marinade for the chicken.
3. Brush the chicken breasts with the marinade, coating them evenly.
4. Place the chicken on the preheated grill and cook for about 5 minutes per side until cooked through and no longer pink in the center. Remove from heat and let it rest for a few minutes.
5. Cut the grilled chicken breasts into slender pieces.
6. Lay the whole wheat wraps or tortillas flat on a clean surface.
7. Divide the sliced avocado, fresh spinach leaves, sliced red onions, and grilled chicken equally among the wraps.
8. If desired, spread a thin layer of Greek yogurt or sour cream on each wrap.
9. Fold the sides of the wraps inward, then roll them tightly to form a wrap.
10. Slice the wraps in half diagonally and serve.

SALMON AND QUINOA STUFFED ZUCCHINI

 Prep time
15 Min

 Cook Time
30 Min

 Servings
4

Nutrition Information

Calories: 380, Protein: 44g,
Carbs: 30g, Fat: 14g, Fiber: 6g

Ingredients

- 2 medium zucchinis
- 2 salmon fillets (6 ounces each)
- 1 cup cooked quinoa
- 1/4 cup diced red bell pepper
- 1/4 cup diced yellow bell pepper
- 1/4 cup diced red onion
- 2 tablespoons chopped fresh parsley
- 1 tablespoon lemon juice
- 1 tablespoon olive oil
- Salt and pepper to taste

Directions

1. Set the oven's heat to 375°F (190°C).
2. Slice the zucchinis in half lengthwise. Use a spoon to scoop out the flesh to create a hollow space in the center of each zucchini half. Use a spoon to scoop out the flesh to create a hollow space in the center of each zucchini half. Set aside the zucchini shells.
3. In a mixing bowl, flake the salmon fillets into small pieces.
4. Add the cooked quinoa, diced red and yellow bell peppers, diced red onion, chopped fresh parsley, lime juice, olive oil, salt & pepper to the bowl with the salmon. Mix well to combine all the ingredients.
5. Fill each hollowed-out zucchini shell with the salmon and quinoa mixture, pressing it down gently to pack it.
6. Place the stuffed zucchini on a lightly greased baking sheet lined with parchment paper.
7. Prepare in the preheated oven for about 25-30 minutes, or until the zucchinis are tender and the filling is cooked through.
8. Remove from the oven and let them cool for a few minutes before serving.

TOFU AND VEGETABLE SKEWERS WITH QUINOA

 Prep time
20 Min

 Cook Time
15 Min

 Servings
2

Nutrition Information

Calories: 400, Protein: 42g,
Carbs: 32g, Fat: 10g, Fiber: 7g

Ingredients

- 8 ounces firm tofu, cut into cubes
- 1 zucchini, cut into thick slices
- 1 bell pepper, cut into chunks
- 1 red onion, cut into chunks
- 8 cherry tomatoes
- 2 tablespoons olive oil
- 2 tablespoons soy sauce
- 1 tablespoon maple syrup or honey
- 1 teaspoon minced garlic
- 1/2 teaspoon ground cumin
- Salt and pepper to taste
- 1 cup cooked quinoa

Directions

1. Adjust the grill or grill pan over medium heat.
2. Whisk together the olive oil, soy sauce, maple syrup or honey, minced garlic, ground cumin, salt and pepper to make a marinade in a small bowl.
3. Thread the tofu cubes, zucchini slices, bell pepper chunks, red onion chunks, and cherry tomatoes onto skewers.
4. Brush the marinade onto the skewered tofu and vegetables, coating them evenly.
5. To cook your skewers, place them on the grill that has been preheated. Cook for 10-15 minutes, occasionally turning them until the tofu turns golden and the vegetables become tender.
6. While the skewers are grilling, cook the quinoa according to the instructions.
7. Serve the tofu and vegetable skewers over a bed of cooked quinoa.

CHICKEN AND BROWN RICE SOUP

Prep time
15 Min

Cook Time
30 Min

Servings
4

Nutrition Information

Calories: 400, Protein: 44g,
Carbs: 38g, Fat: 15g, Fiber: 9g

Ingredients

- 1 tablespoon olive oil
- 1 onion, diced
- 2 cloves garlic, minced
- 2 carrots, diced
- 2 celery stalks, diced
- 4 cups low-sodium chicken broth
- 2 cups cooked chicken breast, shredded
- 1 cup cooked brown rice
- 1 teaspoon dried thyme
- Salt and pepper to taste
- Fresh parsley for garnish

Directions

1. The oil should be heated in a large saucepan over medium heat. Sauté onion and garlic until aromatic.
2. Add diced carrots and celery and simmer for 5 more minutes, stirring regularly.
3. Add chicken broth and boil. Simmer for 15 minutes at low heat to blend flavors.
4. Add shredded chicken breast, cooked brown rice, dried thyme, salt, and pepper to the pot. Combine everything by giving it a thorough stir.
5. Heat chicken and rice for 5 more minutes.
6. Take the dish off the heat and sprinkle it with fresh chopped parsley.
7. Serve hot, and enjoy!

SHRIMP AND QUINOA SALAD WITH LEMON VINAIGRETTE

 Prep time
15 Min

 Cook Time
15 Min

 Servings
2

Nutrition Information

Calories: 400, Protein: 46g,
Carbs: 35g, Fat: 12g, Fiber: 6g

Ingredients

For the salad:
- 8 ounces of cooked shrimp, peeled and deveined
- 1 cup cooked quinoa
- 1 cup cherry tomatoes, halved
- 1 cucumber, diced
- 1/4 red onion, thinly sliced
- 2 tablespoons chopped fresh parsley
- 2 tablespoons chopped fresh mint
- Salt and pepper to taste

For the lemon vinaigrette:
- 2 tablespoons freshly squeezed lemon juice
- 1 tablespoon extra-virgin olive oil
- 1 teaspoon Dijon mustard
- 1 teaspoon honey or maple syrup
- Salt and pepper to taste

Directions

1. Combine the cooked shrimp, quinoa, cherry tomatoes, cucumber, red onion, parsley, and mint in a large bowl.
2. The dressing is made by whisking together lemon juice, olive oil, Dijon mustard, honey or maple syrup, salt, and pepper in a separate bowl.
3. Toss shrimp and quinoa salad with vinaigrette.
4. If you want, you can add more salt and pepper.
5. Let the salad marinate in the fridge for 15 minutes before serving to blend tastes.
6. Serve chilled as a refreshing and protein-packed salad.

LEAN BEEF BURGERS

 Prep time
15 Min

 Cook Time
15 Min

 Servings
4

Nutrition Information

Calories: 444, Protein: 40g,
Carb: 26g, Fat: 20g, Fiber: 4g

Ingredients

- 500g lean ground beef
- Salt and pepper to taste
- 4 whole wheat hamburger buns
- Lettuce, tomato, onion, pickles, and condiments as desired

Directions

1. Preheat the grill to medium-high heat.
2. Powder the ground beef with salt and crushed pepper, then shape it into four patties.
3. Grill the patties for about 5-7 minutes on each side or until they reach your desired level of doneness.
4. Serve the burgers with whole wheat buns with your choice of toppings.

BEEF AND QUINOA STIR-FRY

 Prep time
15 Min

 Cook Time
20 Min

 Servings
2

Nutrition Information
Calories: 450, Protein: 45g,
Carb: 40g, Fat: 15g, Fiber: 6g

Ingredients
- 8 oz lean beef (such as sirloin or tenderloin), thinly sliced
- 1 cup cooked quinoa
- 1 cup broccoli florets
- 1 red bell pepper, thinly sliced
- 1 carrot, julienned
- 2 tablespoons low-sodium soy sauce
- 1 tablespoon hoisin sauce
- 1 tablespoon sesame oil
- 2 cloves garlic, minced
- 1 teaspoon ginger, minced
- 2 green onions, sliced (for garnish)
- Sesame seeds (for garnish)

Directions
1. In a small bowl, mix together the soy sauce, hoisin sauce, and sesame oil to create the stir-fry sauce. Set aside.
2. Heat a large skillet or wok over high heat. Add a splash of oil and quickly stir-fry the beef until browned and cooked to your preference. Remove the beef from the skillet and set aside.
3. In the same skillet, add a bit more oil if needed. Add the minced garlic and ginger, and stir-fry for about 30 seconds until fragrant. Add the broccoli, bell pepper, and carrot. Stir-fry for about 3-4 minutes until the vegetables are slightly tender.
4. Push the vegetables to the side of the skillet and add the cooked quinoa. Pour the stir-fry sauce over the quinoa and mix everything together.
5. Add the cooked beef back to the skillet and stir-fry for an additional 2-3 minutes to heat everything through and allow the flavors to meld.
6. Divide the stir-fry into serving bowls. Garnish with sliced green onions and sesame seeds for added flavor and crunch.

DINNER

CHICKEN SHAWARMA WITH TZATZIKI SAUCE

Prep time
10 Min

Cook Time
15 Min

Servings
4

Nutrition Information

Calories: 310, Protein: 40g,
Carbs: 10g, Fat: 12g, Fiber: 1g

Ingredients

- 500g skinless, boneless chicken breasts
- 2 tbsp olive oil
- 2 tsp cumin
- 2 tsp paprika
- 1 tsp allspice
- 4 garlic cloves, minced
- Juice of 1 lemon
- Salt and pepper to taste
- For the Tzatziki: To make a delicious yogurt dip, you'll need a cup of Greek yogurt, one grated and deseeded cucumber, two minced garlic cloves, a tablespoon of lemon juice, two tablespoons of chopped fresh dill, and salt to your liking.

Directions

1. In a bowl, combine olive oil, cumin, paprika, allspice, minced garlic, lime juice, and salt & pepper. Add chicken breasts, ensuring they are well coated. Cover and let sit for at least an hour, but better yet, overnight.
2. Preheat the grill over moderate-high heat. Grill the chicken for 6-7 minutes per side or until cooked.
3. Combine Greek yogurt, cucumber, garlic, lemon juice, dill, and salt in a bowl for the Tzatziki sauce.
4. Serve the chicken with Tzatziki sauce on the side.

MEXICAN SHRIMP DIABLO

Prep time
10 Min

Cook Time
15 Min

Servings
4

Nutrition Information

Calories: 280, Protein: 40g,
Carbs: 10g, Fat: 10g, Fiber: 2g

Ingredients

- 500g large shrimp, peeled and deveined
- 2 tbsp olive oil
- 1 small onion, chopped
- 2 cloves garlic, minced
- 2 chipotle peppers in adobo sauce, chopped
- 1 can diced tomatoes
- Salt and pepper to taste

Directions

1. Medium-heat olive oil in a big pan. Sauté onion and garlic till transparent.
2. Stir in the diced tomatoes and chipotle chiles. Cook for roughly five minutes.
3. Add shrimp to the skillet. Cook shrimp for 5 minutes until it gets pink and done. Salt and pepper.
4. If desirable, serve with a side of rice.

BUTTER CHICKEN WITH BASMATI RICE

Prep time
10 Min

Cook Time
25 Min

Servings
4

Nutrition Information

Calories: 460, Protein: 40g,
Carbs: 40g, Fat: 15g, Fiber: 4g

Ingredients

- 500g chicken breast, cut into pieces
- 2 tbsp butter
- 1 onion, chopped
- 2 cloves garlic, minced
- 1 tbsp grated fresh ginger
- 1 tbsp garam masala
- 1 tsp turmeric
- 1 tsp cumin
- 1 can crushed tomatoes
- 1 cup heavy cream
- Salt to taste
- Cooked basmati rice for serving

Directions

1. In a large-sized pan, melt butter over medium heat. Add onion, garlic, and ginger, and sauté until the onion is soft.
2. Add garam masala, turmeric, and cumin to the pan, and stir well. Add chicken chunks to the pan, and cook until chicken is browned on all sides.
3. Add crushed tomatoes to the pan, cover, and simmer for about 15 minutes.
4. Add heavy cream to the mix and then season with salt. Cook for an additional 5 minutes.
5. Serve hot cooked basmati rice.

BEEF TAGINE WITH APRICOTS AND ALMONDS

Prep time
20 Min

Cook Time
2 Hour

Servings
4

Nutrition Information

Calories: 510, Protein: 40g,
Carbs: 35g, Fat: 25g, Fiber: 7g

Ingredients

- 500g lean beef, cut into cubes
- 2 tbsp olive oil
- 1 onion, chopped
- 2 cloves garlic, minced
- 2 tsp ground cumin
- 2 tsp ground coriander
- 1 tsp ground cinnamon
- 1 cup dried apricots
- 1/4 cup blanched almonds
- 2 cups beef broth
- Salt and pepper to taste

Directions

1. Warm olive oil in a large-size pan or tagine over medium heat. Place the beef into the cooking vessel until it gets browned on all sides.
2. Place the chopped onion and garlic into the heated pan and cook until tender. Add the spices and stir well.
3. Add the apricots, almonds, and beef broth to the pan. Take to a simmer, then turn the heat to low, cover, and prepare for about 2 hours or until the beef is tender.
4. Season with salt and pepper. Serve hot, garnished with fresh coriander if desired.

MISO GLAZED SALMON

Prep time
10 Min

Cook Time
15 Min

Servings
4

Nutrition Information

Calories: 370, Protein: 40g,
Carbs: 10g, Fat: 18g, Fiber: 1g

Ingredients

- 4 salmon fillets
- 2 tbsp white miso
- 2 tbsp soy sauce
- 1 tbsp mirin
- 1 tbsp sugar
- 1 tsp grated fresh ginger
- Sesame seeds for garnish

Directions

1. Combine miso, soy sauce, mirin, sugar, and ginger in a bowl. Add salmon fillets, ensuring they are well coated. Cover and marinate for at least 30 minutes, preferably overnight.
2. Preheat the broiler. Lay the salmon on a broiler pan and broil for about 7-8 minutes, or until the salmon is cooked to your liking and the glaze is caramelized.
3. Sprinkle with sesame seeds before serving.

JERK CHICKEN WITH COCONUT RICE

 Prep time
20 Min

 Cook Time
40 Min

 Servings
4

Nutrition Information

Calories: 510, Protein: 40g,
Carbs: 40g, Fat: 20g, Fiber: 1g

Ingredients

- 500g chicken breast
- 2 tbsp jerk seasoning
- 2 tbsp olive oil
- 1 cup jasmine rice
- 1 can of coconut milk
- Salt and pepper to taste

Directions

1. Rub chicken breasts with jerk seasoning, olive oil, salt, and pepper. Cover and marinate for at least 2 hours, preferably overnight.
2. Preheat the grill over moderate-high heat. Grill the chicken for 6-7 mins on each side or until cooked.
3. In a pot, bring the coconut milk to a boil. Add rice, turn heat to lower, cover, and prepare for 20 mins or until rice is tender and liquid has been absorbed.
4. Serve the chicken over coconut rice.

BLACK PEPPER BEEF STIR-FRY

Prep time
15 Min

Cook Time
15 Min

Servings
4

Nutrition Information

Calories: 350, Protein: 40g,
Carbs: 20g, Fat: 12g, Fiber: 3g

Ingredients

- 500g lean beef, thinly sliced
- 2 tbsp soy sauce
- 2 tbsp oyster sauce
- 2 tbsp black pepper
- 1 tbsp vegetable oil
- 1 onion, sliced
- 1 bell pepper, sliced
- 1 garlic clove, minced

Directions

1. Combine beef, soy sauce, oyster sauce, and black pepper in a bowl. Mix well.
2. Warm oil in a wok over high heat. Add beef and stir-fry until browned. Remove from the wok.
3. In the same wok, add onion, bell pepper, and garlic. Stir-fry until vegetables are tender.
4. Return beef to the wok and stir-fry for 2-3 minutes.
5. Serve hot with rice if desired.

THAI TOFU GREEN CURRY

Prep time
10 Min

Cook Time
20 Min

Servings
4

Nutrition Information

Calories: 410, Protein: 40g,
Carbs: 20g, Fat: 22g, Fiber: 5g

Ingredients

- 500g firm tofu, cubed
- 2 tbsp vegetable oil
- 2 tbsp green curry paste
- 1 can of coconut milk
- 1 bell pepper, sliced
- 1 carrot, sliced
- 1 zucchini, sliced
- 1 cup Thai basil leaves

Directions

1. Warm oil in a pan over moderate heat. Add curry paste and prepare for 2 minutes until fragrant.
2. Add coconut milk, bell pepper, carrot, zucchini, and tofu. Take to a simmer and cook for about 15 minutes, until vegetables are tender.
3. Stir in Thai basil leaves and serve hot with jasmine rice.

OSSO BUCO WITH GREMOLATA

Prep time
15 Min

Cook Time
2 Hour

Servings
4

Nutrition Information

Calories: 500, Protein: 40g,
Carbs: 15g, Fat: 30g, Fiber: 3g

Ingredients

- 4 pieces of beef osso buco
- 1 onion, chopped
- 2 carrots, chopped
- 2 cloves garlic, minced
- 1 cup red wine
- 1 can crushed tomatoes
- 2 cups beef broth
- Salt and pepper to taste
- To make the gremolata: zest of 1 lemon, 2 cloves garlic (minced), 2 tbsp mashed fresh parsley

Directions

1. Season osso buco with salt and pepper. In a large pan, sear osso buco on all sides until browned. Remove from the pan.
2. In the same pan, add onion, carrots, and garlic. Saute until vegetables are softened.
3. Pour red wine into the pan and use a scraper to collect any browned bits that may be formed on the bottom of the pan. Add crushed tomatoes and beef broth.
4. Return osso buco to the pan. Take to a simmer, then turn heat to low, cover, and prepare for about 2 hours or until meat is tender.
5. Combine lime zest, garlic, and parsley in a small bowl for the gremolata.
6. Serve osso buco sprinkled with gremolata.

GREEK-STYLE BAKED COD WITH LEMON AND GARLIC

Prep time
10 Min

Cook Time
25 Min

Servings
4

Nutrition Information

Calories: 240, Protein: 40g,
Carbs: 5g, Fat: 8g, Fiber: 1g

Ingredients

- 4 cod fillets
- Juice of 1 lemon
- 4 cloves garlic, minced
- 2 tbsp olive oil
- 1 tbsp dried oregano
- Salt and pepper to taste

Directions

1. Preheat oven to 400°F (200°C). In a baking dish, place cod fillets. Drizzle with lemon juice and olive oil. Sprinkle with minced garlic, oregano, salt, and pepper.
2. Bake for about 20-25 minutes or until the cod is flaky and cooked through.
3. If preferred, you may have it hot and pair it with some roasted potatoes on the side.

CHICKEN WITH GREEN SAUCE

Prep time
15 Min

Cook Time
45 Min

Servings
4

Nutrition Information

Calories: 410, Protein: 40g,
Carbs: 5g, Fat: 25g, Fiber: 1g

Ingredients

- 500g chicken breast
- 2 tbsp olive oil
- 2 tsp cumin
- 2 tsp paprika
- 4 garlic cloves, minced
- Juice of 2 limes
- Salt and pepper to taste
- For the green sauce: 1 jalapeno, 1 bunch cilantro, 2 cloves garlic, 1/2 cup mayonnaise, juice of 1 lime

Directions

1. Combine olive oil, cumin, paprika, minced garlic, lime juice, salt, and pepper in a bowl. Add chicken breasts, ensuring they are well coated. Cover and marinate for 1 hour, preferably overnight.
2. Preheat the grill over normal-high heat. Cook the chicken on the grill for 6-7 minutes on each side or until fully cooked.
3. Blend jalapeno, cilantro, garlic, mayonnaise, and lime juice for the green sauce until smooth.
4. Serve the chicken hot with green sauce on the side.

PAELLA WITH SEAFOOD AND CHICKEN

Prep time
20 Min

Cook Time
40 Min

Servings
4

Nutrition Information

Calories: 450, Protein: 40g,
Carbs: 50g, Fat: 10g, Fiber: 3g

Ingredients

- 200g chicken breast, cut into pieces
- 200g mixed seafood (like shrimp, mussels, and calamari)
- 1 onion, chopped
- 2 cloves garlic, minced
- 1 bell pepper, chopped
- 1 cup paella rice
- 1/4 tsp saffron threads
- 2 cups chicken broth
- Salt and pepper to taste
- Fresh parsley and lemon wedges for serving

Directions

1. Warm oil in a paella pan or large skillet over medium heat. Add the chicken and cook until browned. Remove from the pan.
2. In a pan, add onion, garlic, and bell pepper. Saute until soft.
3. Add rice and saffron to the pan, stirring to coat the rice. Cook for about 2 minutes.
4. Add chicken broth, cooked chicken, and mixed seafood to the pan. Bring to a simmer and cook for about 20 minutes, until rice is soft and liquid is absorbed.
5. To enjoy, serve the dish hot and add a finishing touch of fresh parsley and lemon wedges.

PHO WITH BEEF AND TOFU

Prep time
15 Min

Cook Time
30 Min

Servings
4

Nutrition Information

Calories: 500, Protein: 40g,
Carbs: 55g, Fat: 15g, Fiber: 3g

Ingredients

- 500g lean beef, thinly sliced
- 200g firm tofu, cubed
- 4 cups beef broth
- 2 tbsp fish sauce
- 1 onion, thinly sliced
- 2 cloves garlic, minced
- 2-star anise
- 1 cinnamon stick
- 4 servings of rice noodles
- Fresh basil, cilantro, bean sprouts, and lime wedges for serving

Directions

1. Combine beef broth, fish sauce, onion, garlic, star anise, and cinnamon stick in a large pot. Take to a simmer and cook for about 15 minutes.
2. Add beef and tofu to the pot and cook for 10 minutes until the beef is cooked to your liking.
3. Cook rice noodles according to package instructions. Divide among bowls.
4. Ladle the soup over the noodles. Serve with fresh herbs, bean sprouts, and lime wedges on the side.

TUSCAN BEEF AND WHITE BEAN STEW

Prep time
15 Min

Cook Time
1 hr 30 Min

Servings
4

Nutrition Information

Calories: 450, Protein: 40g,
Carbs: 40g, Fat: 15g, Fiber: 10g

Ingredients

- 500g lean beef, cut into chunks
- 1 onion, chopped
- 2 carrots, chopped
- 2 cloves garlic, minced
- 1 can white beans, drained and rinsed
- 1 can crushed tomatoes
- 2 cups beef broth
- 1 tsp dried thyme
- Salt and pepper to taste

Directions

1. In a large pot, brown the beef on all sides. Remove from the pot.
2. In the same pot, sauté the onion, carrots, and garlic until softened.
3. Return the beef to the pot. Add the white beans, crushed tomatoes, beef broth, and dried thyme. Season with salt and pepper.
4. Take to a boil, then reduce the heat and simmer 1 hour and 30 minutes until the beef is tender.
5. If desired, you can choose to sprinkle parmesan cheese on top of the hot dish.

CHICKEN WITH COUSCOUS

 Prep time
20 Min

 Cook Time
40 Min

 Servings
4

Nutrition Information

Calories: 450, Protein: 40g,
Carbs: 50g, Fat: 10g, Fiber: 8g

Ingredients

- 500g chicken breast, cut into pieces
- 1 tbsp Moroccan spice blend
- 2 tbsp olive oil
- 1 onion, chopped
- 2 cloves garlic, minced
- 1 can chickpeas, drained and rinsed
- 1 can diced tomatoes
- 1 cup couscous
- 2 cups chicken broth
- Salt and pepper to taste

Directions

1. Toss the chicken pieces with the Moroccan spice blend, salt, and pepper. Warm the olive oil in a large-sized skillet; next, place the chicken in the skillet and cook until all sides are browned. Once done, remove the chicken from the skillet.
2. In the same skillet, sauté the onion and garlic until softened. Add the chickpeas and diced tomatoes, then return the chicken to the skillet.
3. In another pot, take the chicken broth to a boil. Add the couscous, then remove from heat and let stand for 5 minutes until the liquid is absorbed.
4. If desired, serve the chicken with the couscous, with a sprinkle of fresh cilantro.

MISO SALMON

Prep time
15 Min

Cook Time
20 Min

Servings
4

Nutrition Information

Calories: 300, Protein: 40g,
Carbs: 15g, Fat: 10g, Fiber: 2g

Ingredients

- 4 salmon fillets
- 3 tbsp miso paste
- 2 tbsp soy sauce
- 1 tbsp rice vinegar
- 1 tbsp honey
- 1 tbsp ginger, grated
- 2 cloves garlic, minced

Directions

1. Mix the miso paste, soy sauce, rice vinegar, honey, ginger, and garlic in a bowl to make the marinade.
2. Marinate the salmon fillets in the blend for at least 1 hour or overnight.
3. Set the oven's heat to 400°F (200°C) and place a baking sheet with foil. Place the marinated salmon fillets on the foil and bake for 15-20 minutes until the salmon gets fully cooked.
4. Serve with steamed rice and vegetables if preferred.

BEEF AND VEGETABLE STIR-FRY

Prep time
20 Min

Cook Time
20 Min

Servings
4

Nutrition Information

Calories: 350, Protein: 40g,
Carbs: 20g, Fat: 15g, Fiber: 4g

Ingredients

- 500g lean beef, thinly sliced
- 1 bell pepper, sliced
- 1 carrot, sliced
- 1 zucchini, sliced
- 2 cloves garlic, minced
- 1 tbsp ginger, minced
- 2 tbsp soy sauce
- 1 tbsp oyster sauce
- 1 tbsp of cornstarch blended with 2 tbsp water
- Salt and pepper to taste
- 2 tbsp vegetable oil

Directions

1. Over high heat, warm 1 tablespoon of oil in a wok or big skillet. Stir-fry the beef until it is almost done. Take out of the wok and put it to the side.
2. Add another tablespoon of oil to the same pot. Stir fry the bell pepper, carrot, and zucchini until soft.
3. Once you have added the garlic and ginger, stir until you can smell their delightful aroma. Put the beef back in the pot.
4. Mix in soy and oyster sauce, then add the cornstarch mixture. Stir until the sauce has thickened.
5. Season with salt and pepper. Serve hot with steamed rice if desired.

TOFU AND BROCCOLI STIR-FRY

 Prep time
15 Min

 Cook Time
20 Min

 Servings
4

Nutrition Information

Calories: 300, Protein: 40g,
Carbs: 25g, Fat: 8g, Fiber: 5g

Ingredients

- 400g firm tofu, cubed
- 1 head of broccoli, cut into florets
- 2 cloves garlic, minced
- 1 tbsp ginger, minced
- 2 tbsp soy sauce
- 1 tbsp hoisin sauce
- 2 tbsp vegetable oil
- Sesame seeds for garnish

Directions

1. Heat 1 tablespoon of oil over high in a large skillet or wok heat. Stir-fry the tofu until it turns golden brown. Please take out the ingredients from the wok and keep them aside.
2. In the same wok, add a tbsp of oil. Stir-fry the broccoli until it is just tender.
3. Stir in the garlic and ginger until aromatic. Bring the tofu back to the wok.
4. Mix in the soy and hoisin sauce until everything is well coated.
5. Garnish with sesame seeds. Serve hot with steamed rice if desired.

CHICKEN PICCATA

Prep time
10 Min

Cook Time
20 Min

Servings
4

Nutrition Information

Calories: 300, Protein: 40g,
Carbs: 8g, Fat: 12g, Fiber: 1g

Ingredients

- 500g chicken breast, cut into cutlets
- 2 tbsp flour
- Salt and pepper to taste
- 2 tbsp olive oil
- 2 cloves garlic, minced
- 1/2 cup chicken broth
- Juice of 1 lemon
- 2 tbsp capers
- 2 tbsp fresh parsley, chopped

Directions

1. To prepare the chicken cutlets, first season them with salt and pepper. Then, coat them in flour by rolling them over them.
2. Medium-heat olive oil in a skillet. Cook chicken till browned and done. Take the food out of the pan.
3. Cook garlic in the same skillet until fragrant. Chicken broth, lemon juice, and capers. Bring to a boil, then let it simmer for about 5 minutes.
4. Pour sauce over chicken and return to skillet.
5. Sprinkle with fresh parsley before serving.

GRILLED LAMB CHOPS WITH MINT CHIMICHURRI

Prep time
20 Min

Cook Time
10 Min

Servings
4

Nutrition Information

Calories: 550, Protein: 40g,
Carbs: 5g, Fat: 42g, Fiber: 2g

Ingredients

- 8 lamb chops
- 1/2 cup olive oil
- Juice of 1 lemon
- 2 cloves garlic, minced
- Salt and pepper to taste
- 1 cup fresh mint leaves
- 1 cup fresh parsley leaves
- 1/4 cup red wine vinegar
- 1/4 cup olive oil

Directions

1. Mix 1/2 cup olive oil, lime juice, garlic, salt, and pepper in a bowl. To marinate the lamb chops, add them to the mixture and let it sit for at least 1 hour or overnight.
2. To make the chimichurri, blend the mint, parsley, red wine vinegar, and 1/4 cup oil until smooth.
3. Set a grill or grill pan over medium-high heat. Grill the lamb chops for about 3-4 minutes per side or until cooked to your liking.
4. Serve the lamb chops with the mint chimichurri on the side.

SZECHUAN TOFU AND GREEN BEANS

 Prep time
15 Min

 Cook Time
20 Min

 Servings
4

Nutrition Information

Calories: 300, Protein: 40g,
Carbs: 20g, Fat: 10g, Fiber: 6g

Ingredients

- 400g firm tofu, cubed
- 500g green beans, trimmed
- 2 tbsp vegetable oil
- 2 cloves garlic, minced
- 1 tbsp ginger, minced
- 2 tbsp soy sauce
- 1 tbsp rice vinegar
- 1 tsp Szechuan peppercorns, crushed

Directions

1. Prepare the oil by heating one tablespoon in a wok or a big pan set over high heat. Stir-fry tofu till browned. Take out of the wok, and put it to the side.
2. Please add one more tablespoon of oil to the wok. Stir-fry green beans till soft.
3. Stir garlic and ginger until fragrant. Return tofu to wok.
4. Add soy sauce, rice vinegar, and crushed Szechuan peppercorns.
5. Stir until everything is well coated.
6. Serve hot with steamed rice if desired.

GRILLED CHICKEN WITH PEACH SALSA

Prep time
15 Min

Cook Time
15 Min

Servings
4

Nutrition Information

Calories: 320, Protein: 40g,
Carbs: 15g, Fat: 12g, Fiber: 2g

Ingredients

- 500g chicken breast
- Juice of 1 lime
- 2 tbsp olive oil
- Salt and pepper to taste
- 2 ripe peaches, diced
- 1/4 cup red onion, diced
- 1 jalapeno, seeded and minced
- 2 tbsp fresh cilantro, chopped

Directions

1. Combine the lime juice, olive oil, salt, and pepper in a basin. Marinate the chicken breasts for one hour or overnight.
2. Peach salsa comprises diced peaches, red onion, jalapeno, and cilantro.
3. Heat a grill or griddle pan to moderate-high temperatures. Griddle the chicken for 5 to 7 minutes per side or until thoroughly cooked.
4. Serve the chicken with the peach salsa on top.

SHRIMP AND PINEAPPLE FRIED RICE

 Prep time
15 Min

 Cook Time
20 Min

 Servings
4

Nutrition Information

Calories: 400, Protein: 40g,
Carbs: 40g, Fat: 10g, Fiber: 3g

Ingredients

- 500g shrimp, peeled and deveined
- 2 cups cooked rice
- 1 cup pineapple chunks
- 1 bell pepper, diced
- 1 carrot, diced
- 2 cloves garlic, minced
- 2 tbsp soy sauce
- 1 tbsp fish sauce
- 2 tbsp vegetable oil
- 2 eggs, beaten

Directions

1. Warm one tbsp of oil in a large wok or large skillet over high heat. Add the shrimp and stir-fry until pink. Remove from the wok and set aside.
2. Add one more tablespoon of oil to the same wok to continue cooking. Then, add the bell pepper and carrot, and stir-fry them until they are just tender.
3. Add the garlic, stirring until fragrant. Add the rice and pineapple chunks, stirring to mix well.
4. Push the rice to one side of the wok and pour the beaten eggs on the other. Scramble the eggs, then mix with the rice.
5. Return the shrimp, soy sauce, and fish sauce to the wok. Keep stirring until all the ingredients are evenly coated and heated thoroughly.
6. Serve hot.

GARLIC HERB ROASTED CHICKEN

Prep time
5 Min

Cook Time
1 Hour

Servings
4

Nutrition Information

Calories: 500, Protein: 40g,
Carbs: 5g, Fat: 35g, Fiber: 2g

Ingredients

- 1 whole chicken (about 1.5kg)
- 4 cloves garlic, minced
- 2 tbsp fresh rosemary, minced
- 2 tbsp fresh thyme, minced
- 2 tbsp olive oil
- Salt and pepper to taste
- 1 lemon, sliced
- 2 sprigs rosemary
- 2 sprigs thyme

Directions

1. Preheat the oven to 190C (375F).
2. Mix the minced garlic, rosemary, thyme, olive oil, salt, and pepper.
3. Rub the garlic herb blend all over the chicken, inside and out.
4. Stuff the cavity of the chicken with the sliced lemon and sprigs of rosemary and thyme.
5. Set the chicken on a roasting rack in a roasting pan. Roast for about 1 hour or until the internal temperature reaches 74C (165F).
6. Leave the chicken to cool for 10 minutes before carving. Serve with desired side dishes.

LAMB KOFTA WITH TZATZIKI

Prep time
25 Min

Cook Time
15 Min

Servings
4

Nutrition Information

Calories: 550, Protein: 40g,
Carbs: 10g, Fat: 40g, Fiber: 2g

Ingredients

- 500g ground lamb
- 1 small onion, finely chopped
- 2 cloves garlic, minced
- 2 tbsp fresh parsley, chopped
- 1 tsp ground cumin
- 1/2 tsp ground coriander
- Salt and pepper to taste
- To make Tzatziki: 1 cup Greek yogurt, 1 small cucumber, grated and drained, 2 cloves garlic, minced, 1 tbsp fresh dill, chopped, Juice of 1/2 lemon, salt to taste

Directions

1. Mix the ground lamb, onion, garlic, parsley, cumin, coriander, salt, and pepper in a bowl. Form into 8 oval-shaped patties.
2. Heat a grill or grill pan over moderate-high heat. Grill the lamb kofta for about 5-6 minutes per side or until cooked to your liking.
3. Mix the Greek yogurt, grated cucumber, garlic, dill, lemon juice, and salt to make the tzatziki.
4. Serve the lamb kofta with the tzatziki on the side.

PAN-SEARED TOFU WITH BOK CHOY AND GINGER SOY SAUCE

 Prep time
15 Min

 Cook Time
20 Min

 Servings
4

Nutrition Information

Calories: 300, Protein: 40g,
Carbs: 15g, Fat: 10g, Fiber: 5g

Ingredients

- 400g firm tofu, sliced into slabs
- 500g bok choy, trimmed
- 2 cloves garlic, minced
- 1 tbsp ginger, minced
- 2 tbsp soy sauce
- 1 tbsp rice vinegar
- 2 tbsp vegetable oil

Directions

1. First, heat one tablespoon of oil in a skillet on medium heat. Place the tofu in the pan and cook each side until golden brown. Remove from the skillet and set aside.
2. In the same non-stick skillet, add another tbsp of oil. Add the bok choy and stir-fry until just tender.
3. Add garlic and ginger to the skillet and stir until you can smell their fragrant aroma. Afterward, mix in the soy sauce and rice vinegar.
4. Return the tofu to the skillet, spooning the sauce over the top. Simmer for a few minutes until everything is well coated and heated through.
5. Serve hot with steamed rice if desired.

BAKED LEMON HERB SALMON

 Prep time
10 Min

 Cook Time
15 Min

 Servings
4

Nutrition Information

Calories: 350, Protein: 40g,
Carbs: 2g, Fat: 20g, Fiber: 0g

Ingredients

- 4 salmon fillets (about 150g each)
- 2 tbsp olive oil
- Juice of 1 lemon
- 2 cloves garlic, minced
- 2 tbsp fresh dill, chopped
- Salt and pepper to taste

Directions

1. Preheat the oven to 200C (400F).
2. Lay the salmon fillets on an aluminum foil. Drizzle with oil and lime juice, then sprinkle with garlic, dill, salt, and pepper.
3. Bake for about 15 minutes or until the salmon is cooked through.
4. Place a dash of fresh lime juice and serve with your preferred side dishes.

GRILLED CHICKEN CAESAR SALAD

 Prep time
20 Min

 Cook Time
15 Min

 Servings
4

Nutrition Information

Calories: 350, Protein: 40g,
Carbs: 10g, Fat: 18g, Fiber: 3g

Ingredients

- 500g chicken breast
- 1/2 cup Caesar dressing
- 2 heads romaine lettuce, chopped
- 1 cup cherry tomatoes, halved
- 1/2 cup Parmesan cheese, shaved
- Salt and pepper to taste

Directions

1. Marinate the chicken breast in half of the Caesar dressing for at least 1 hour or overnight.
2. Heat a grill or grill pan over moderate-high heat. Grill the chicken for 5-7 minutes per side or until cooked through. Slice into strips.
3. Combine the chopped lettuce, cherry tomatoes, and grilled chicken in a large bowl. Drizzle with the remaining Caesar dressing and toss to coat.
4. Sprinkle with shaved Parmesan before serving.

BEEF AND BROCCOLI STIR FRY

 Prep time
15 Min

 Cook Time
20

 Servings
4

Nutrition Information

Calories: 400, Protein: 40g,
Carbs: 20g, Fat: 20g, Fiber: 6g

Ingredients

- 500g lean beef strips
- 500g broccoli florets
- 2 cloves garlic, minced
- 1 tbsp ginger, minced
- 2 tbsp soy sauce
- 1 tbsp oyster sauce
- 2 tbsp vegetable oil

Directions

1. Warm 1 tablespoon of oil over high heat in a wok or big skillet. Stir-fry the beef until it is just browned. Take out of the wok and put it to the side.
2. Add another tablespoon of oil to the same pot. Stir-fry the broccoli until it is just done.
3. Stir the garlic and ginger into the wok until they start to fragrance good. Put the beef back in the pot.
4. Mix in the soy and oyster sauce to coat the beef and broccoli.
5. Serve hot with steamed rice if desired.

BAKED TILAPIA WITH TOMATO AND BASIL

Prep time
15 Min

Cook Time
15 Min

Servings
4

Nutrition Information

Calories: 300, Protein: 40g,
Carbs: 5g, Fat: 15g, Fiber: 2g

Ingredients

- 4 tilapia fillets (about 150g each)
- 2 tomatoes, sliced
- 1/4 cup fresh basil leaves
- 2 cloves garlic, minced
- 2 tbsp olive oil
- Salt and pepper to taste

Directions

1. Preheat the oven to 200C (400F).
2. Set the tilapia fillets in a baking dish. Top each fillet with sliced tomatoes, basil leaves, and minced garlic. To prepare, drizzle oil onto your dish and season it with salt and pepper.
3. Bake for about 15 minutes or until the tilapia is cooked through.
4. To get the flavor of your dish, add a fresh lime juice squeeze and any preferred side dishes.

CHICKEN AND MUSHROOM RISOTTO

Prep time
10 Min

Cook Time
30 Min

Servings
4

Nutrition Information

Calories: 500, Protein: 40g,
Carbs: 50g, Fat: 15g, Fiber: 3g

Ingredients

- 500g chicken breast, diced
- 1 cup Arborio rice
- 4 cups chicken broth
- 2 cups sliced mushrooms
- 1 small onion, diced
- 2 cloves garlic, minced
- 2 tbsp olive oil
- 1/2 cup Parmesan cheese, grated
- Salt and pepper to taste

Directions

1. Warm 1 tbsp of olive oil over a medium-high flame in a large skillet. Cook chicken until it is no longer pink. Remove the food from the pan and set aside.
2. In the same pan, add tbsp of olive oil. Prepare the garlic and onion until the onion is translucent.
3. Add the Arborio rice to the skillet, stirring to coat in the oil. Add 1 cup of chicken broth, stirring until absorbed.
4. Continue adding chicken broth, 1 cup at a time, until all the broth has been absorbed and the rice is tender.
5. Return the chicken to the skillet, along with the mushrooms. Stir until the mushrooms are cooked, and everything is heated through.
6. Stir in the grated Parmesan, seasoning with salt and pepper to taste. Serve hot.

LEMON GARLIC SHRIMP PASTA

Prep time
10 Min

Cook Time
20 Min

Servings
4

Nutrition Information

Calories: 450, Protein: 40g,
Carbs: 50g, Fat: 10g, Fiber: 8g

Ingredients

- 500g shrimp, peeled and deveined
- 250g whole wheat spaghetti
- 4 cloves garlic, minced
- Juice of 1 lemon
- Zest of 1 lemon
- 2 tbsp olive oil
- Salt and pepper to taste
- Fresh parsley, chopped for garnish

Directions

1. Cook the spaghetti as per package instructions until al dente. Drain, reserving some pasta water.
2. In the meantime, while the pasta is cooking, warm the olive oil in a large-sized skillet over moderate heat. Add the garlic and cook until fragrant.
3. Add the shrimp to the skillet, seasoning with salt and pepper. Cook until the shrimp gets pink and cooked through.
4. Add the prepared spaghetti to the skillet with the shrimp. Add the lime juice and zest, tossing to combine. Add some of the pasta water you put aside earlier to thin out the sauce.
5. Serve the pasta with a garnish of fresh parsley.

GRILLED TOFU KEBABS WITH PEANUT SAUCE

 Prep time
30 Min

 Cook Time
10 Min

 Servings
4

Nutrition Information

Calories: 400, Protein: 40g,
Carbs: 30g, Fat: 20g, Fiber: 8g

Ingredients

- 400g firm tofu, cubed
- 2 bell peppers, cut into chunks
- 1 zucchini, cut into chunks
- For the marinade: 1/4 cup soy sauce, 2 tbsp sesame oil, 2 tbsp honey, 2 cloves garlic, mashed, 1 tbsp ginger, minced
- For the peanut sauce: 1/2 cup peanut butter, 2 tbsp soy sauce, 2 tbsp lime juice, 1 tbsp honey, 1 tbsp sesame oil, 1-2 tbsp water to thin

Directions

1. Mix the marinade ingredients. Add the cubed tofu, tossing to coat. Let marinate for 30 minutes or up to 2 hours.
2. Set a grill or grill pan over moderate-high heat.
3. Thread the marinated tofu, bell peppers, and zucchini onto skewers.
4. Grill the kebabs for about 5 minutes per side or until the vegetables are tender and the tofu is golden.
5. While the kebabs are grilling, mix the peanut sauce ingredients.
6. Serve the grilled tofu kebabs with the peanut sauce on the side.

LEMON HERB ROASTED COD WITH ASPARAGUS

Prep time
15 Min

Cook Time
20 Min

Servings
4

Nutrition Information

Calories: 350, Protein: 40g
, Carbs: 10g, Fat: 15g, Fiber: 5g

Ingredients

- 4 cod fillets (about 150g each)
- 500g asparagus, trimmed
- 2 lemons, sliced
- 4 cloves garlic, minced
- 2 tbsp fresh parsley, chopped
- 2 tbsp olive oil
- Salt and pepper to taste

Directions

1. Preheat the oven to 200C (400F).
2. Arrange the cod fillets and asparagus on a baking sheet. Drizzle with olive oil and sprinkle with mashed garlic, parsley, salt, and pepper.
3. Arrange lemon slices on top of the cod fillets.
4. Bake for about 20 minutes or until the cod is cooked and the asparagus is tender. Enjoy hot!

BALSAMIC GLAZED CHICKEN AND ROASTED VEGETABLES

Prep time
15 Min

Cook Time
20 Min

Servings
4

Nutrition Information

Calories: 400, Protein: 40g,
Carbs: 30g, Fat: 15g, Fiber: 6g

Ingredients

- 500g chicken breast
- 2 carrots, sliced
- 2 zucchini, sliced
- 1 red bell pepper, sliced
- For the glaze: 1/2 cup balsamic vinegar, 2 tbsp honey, 1 tbsp of Dijon mustard, 2 cloves garlic, chopped
- 2 tbsp olive oil
- Salt and pepper to taste

Directions

1. Preheat the oven to 200C (400F).
2. Set the chicken and vegetables on a baking sheet. To add flavor, lightly drizzle olive oil and sprinkle salt and pepper.
3. Mix the balsamic glaze ingredients and drizzle half over the chicken and vegetables.
4. Prepare for about 20 minutes until the chicken is cooked and the vegetables are tender.
5. Drizzle the remaining balsamic glaze over the cooked chicken and vegetables before serving.

BEEF STIR-FRY WITH GINGER AND SCALLIONS

Prep time
10 Min

Cook Time
20 Min

Servings
4

Nutrition Information

Calories: 400, Protein: 40g,
Carbs: 10g, Fat: 20g, Fiber: 3g

Ingredients

- 500g lean beef strips
- 1 bunch of scallions cut into 2-inch lengths
- 1 tbsp fresh ginger, minced
- 2 cloves garlic, minced
- 2 tbsp soy sauce
- 1 tbsp oyster sauce
- 2 tbsp vegetable oil
- Salt and pepper to taste

Directions

1. High-heat a wok or large skillet with 1 tbsp oil. Stir-fry beef until browned. Set it aside.
2. Please add one more tablespoon of oil to the wok. Stir-fry scallions, ginger, and garlic until aromatic.
3. Return the beef to the wok. Add the soy sauce and oyster sauce, stirring to combine.
4. Season with salt and pepper to taste. Serve hot with steamed rice if desired.

GRILLED LEMON HERB MEDITERRANEAN CHICKEN SALAD

Prep time
20 Min

Cook Time
20 Min

Servings
4

Nutrition Information

Calories: 400, Protein: 40g,
Carbs: 15g, Fat: 20g, Fiber: 5g

Ingredients

- 500g chicken breast
- 1 romaine lettuce, chopped
- 1 cucumber, sliced
- 1 red onion, sliced
- 2 tomatoes, chopped
- 1/2 cup kalamata olives
- 1/2 cup feta cheese, crumbled
- For the marinade/dressing: Juice of 1 lemon, 2 tbsp olive oil, 2 cloves garlic, mashed, 1 tbsp dried oregano, salt & pepper to taste

Directions

1. Mix the marinade/dressing ingredients. Pour half of it over the chicken breasts, letting them marinate for at least 30 minutes.
2. Heat a grill or grill pan over moderate-high heat.
3. Grill the chicken for about 7 minutes per side or until cooked through. Let the chicken rest for a few minutes, then slice.
4. Arrange the lettuce, cucumber, red onion, tomatoes, and olives in a salad bowl. Top with the sliced chicken and feta cheese. Drizzle the remaining dressing over the salad before serving.

THAI RED CURRY WITH TOFU AND VEGETABLES

 Prep time
15 Min

 Cook Time
20 Min

 Servings
4

Nutrition Information

Calories: 400, Protein: 40g,
Carbs: 20g, Fat: 20g, Fiber: 6g

Ingredients

- 400g firm tofu, cubed
- 2 bell peppers, sliced
- 1 zucchini, sliced
- 1 can of coconut milk
- 2 tbsp red curry paste
- 2 tbsp soy sauce
- 1 tbsp vegetable oil
- Steamed rice for serving (optional)

Directions

1. Warm the vegetable oil in a large-size skillet over medium heat. Add the tofu and prepare until golden on all sides. Take away the tofu from the skillet and set aside.
2. In the same skillet, put in the bell peppers and zucchini. Cook until tender.
3. Combine the red curry paste, coconut milk, and soy sauce by stirring them together. Bring to a simmer.
4. Return the tofu to the skillet, stirring to coat in the curry sauce. Let everything simmer together for a few minutes.
5. Serve the curry over steamed rice if desired.

GREEK-STYLE BAKED COD WITH LEMON AND GARLIC

 Prep time
10 Min

 Cook Time
20 Min

 Servings
4

Nutrition Information

Calories: 300, Protein: 40g,
Carbs: 5g, Fat: 15g, Fiber: 2g

Ingredients

- 4 cod fillets (about 150g each)
- Juice of 2 lemons
- 4 cloves garlic, minced
- 2 tbsp olive oil
- 2 tsp dried oregano
- Salt and pepper to taste

Directions

1. Preheat the oven to 200C (400F).
2. Place the pieces of cod in an oven dish. Sprinkle with the chopped garlic, oregano, salt, and pepper. Drizzle with fresh lime juice and olive oil.
3. Bake for about 20 minutes or until the cod is cooked through. Serve hot, and enjoy!

MOROCCAN CHICKPEA AND VEGETABLE TAGINE WITH COUSCOUS

 Prep time
15 Min

 Cook Time
35 Min

 Servings
4

Nutrition Information

Calories: 400, Protein: 40g,
Carbs: 60g, Fat: 10g. Fiber: 10g

Ingredients

- 1 can chickpeas, drained and rinsed
- 2 carrots, sliced
- 1 zucchini, chopped
- 1 red bell pepper, chopped
- 1 onion, chopped
- 4 cloves garlic, minced
- 2 tbsp olive oil
- 1 tsp cumin
- 1 tsp turmeric
- 1/2 tsp cinnamon
- Salt and pepper to taste
- 2 cups vegetable broth
- 1 cup couscous
- Fresh parsley, chopped for garnish

Directions

1. Warm the olive oil in a large-sized pot over moderate heat. Add the onion and garlic, cooking until get softened.
2. Add the carrots, zucchini, and red bell pepper to the pot. Cook for a few minutes until the vegetables start to soften.
3. Stir in the cumin, turmeric, cinnamon, salt, and pepper. Cook for another minute until the spices get fragrant.
4. Add the chickpeas and vegetable broth. Bring to a simmer and cook for about 20 minutes or until the vegetables are tender.
5. In the meantime, cook the couscous as per the package instructions.
6. Serve the tagine over the couscous, garnished with fresh parsley.

SIDE DISHES

BALSAMIC ROASTED BRUSSELS SPROUTS

Prep time
10 Min

Cook Time
20 Min

Servings
1

Nutrition Information

Calories: 170, Protein: 6g,
Carbs: 20g, Fat: 8g, Fiber: 8g

Ingredients

- 200g Brussels sprouts, trimmed and halved
- 1 tbsp olive oil
- 1 tbsp balsamic vinegar
- Salt and pepper to taste

Directions

1. Preheat your oven to 400F. Toss the Brussels sprouts with olive oil, balsamic vinegar, salt, and pepper.
2. To cook the Brussels sprouts, place them on a baking tray and roast them for approximately 20 minutes until they are tender and caramelized.

GARLIC PARMESAN ROASTED BROCCOLI

 Prep time
10 Min

 Cook Time
20 Min

 Servings
1

Nutrition Information

Calories: 220, Protein: 10g,
Carbs: 20g, Fat: 12g, Fiber: 6g

Ingredients

- 1 head of large broccoli, cut into florets
- 2 cloves garlic, minced
- 1 tbsp olive oil
- 2 tbsp grated Parmesan cheese
- Salt and pepper to taste

Directions

1. Preheat your oven to 400F. Toss the broccoli with garlic, olive oil, salt, and pepper.
2. Put the broccoli on a baking sheet and roast it for 20 minutes or until it is soft but still has a bit of a crunch. Sprinkle with Parmesan in the last 5 minutes of cooking.

STEAMED ASPARAGUS WITH LEMON ZEST

Prep time
5 Min

Cook Time
5 Min

Servings
1

Nutrition Information

Calories: 80, Protein: 4g,
Carbs: 8g, Fat: 0g, Fiber: 4g

Ingredients

- 200g asparagus spears, ends trimmed
- Zest of 1 lemon
- Salt and pepper to taste

Directions

1. Steam the asparagus for about 4-5 minutes or until tender but still crisp.
2. Toss the asparagus with lemon zest, salt, and pepper before serving.

CILANTRO LIME QUINOA SALAD

Prep time
10 Min

Cook Time
20 Min

Servings
1

Nutrition Information

Calories: 200, Protein: 6g,
Carbs: 34g, Fat: 4g, Fiber: 4g

Ingredients

- 1/2 cup cooked quinoa
- 1/2 cup chopped fresh cilantro
- Juice of 1 lime
- 1/4 cucumber, diced
- 1/4 bell pepper, diced
- Salt and pepper to taste

Directions

1. Combine the cooked quinoa, cilantro, lime juice, cucumber, and bell pepper in a bowl. Season with salt & pepper and toss well.

GREEK SALAD WITH FETA AND OLIVES

 Prep time
10 Min

 Cook Time
0 Min

 Servings
1

Nutrition Information

Calories: 210, Protein: 6g,
Carbs: 8g, Fat: 16g, Fiber: 3g

Ingredients

- 2 cups mixed salad greens
- 1/4 cucumber, sliced
- 10 cherry tomatoes, halved
- 2 tbsp sliced kalamata olives
- 2 tbsp crumbled feta cheese
- 1 tbsp olive oil
- 1 tbsp lemon juice

Directions

1. Combine the salad greens, cucumber, tomatoes, olives, and feta cheese in a bowl.
2. Drizzle oil and lime juice, season with salt and pepper, and toss well.

TURMERIC ROASTED CAULIFLOWER

Prep time
10 Min

Cook Time
20 Min

Servings
1

Nutrition Information

Calories: 150, Protein: 5g,
Carbs: 15g, Fat: 8g, Fiber: 6g

Ingredients

- 200g cauliflower florets
- 1 tbsp olive oil
- 1/2 tsp ground turmeric
- Salt and pepper to taste

Directions

1. Preheat your oven to 400F. Toss the cauliflower with olive oil, turmeric, salt, and pepper.
2. To prepare the cauliflower, put it on a baking sheet and prepare it for about 20 minutes.
3. The cauliflower should be tender and have a slight crispiness to it when done.

GREEN BEANS ALMONDINE

 Prep time
5 Min

 Cook Time
10 Min

 Servings
1

Nutrition Information

Calories: 180, Protein: 4g,
Carbs: 10g, Fat: 14g, Fiber: 4g

Ingredients

- 1 cup green beans, ends trimmed
- 1 tbsp butter
- 2 tbsp sliced almonds
- Salt and pepper to taste

Directions

1. Steam the green beans for approximately 4 to 5 minutes until they are tender yet firm.
2. Heat the skillet over moderate heat and melt the butter in it. Add the almonds and caramelize them for approximately two to three minutes.
3. To enhance the flavor, add some salt and pepper to the green beans, then add them to the skillet, butter, and hazelnuts.

STEAMED BOK CHOY WITH SOY SAUCE AND GINGER

Prep time
5 Min

Cook Time
5 Min

Servings
1

Nutrition Information

Calories: 50, Protein: 4g,
Carbs: 6g, Fat: 0g, Fiber: 2g

Ingredients

- 200g bok choy, ends trimmed
- 1 tbsp soy sauce
- 1/2 tsp grated ginger

Directions

1. Steam the bok choy until it is tender but still crisp, about 4-5 minutes.
2. To enhance the flavor of the bok choy, add soy sauce and grated ginger before serving.

SESAME ROASTED SNAP PEAS

Prep time
10 Min

Cook Time
15 Min

Servings
1

Nutrition Information

Calories: 160, Protein: 5g,
Carbs: 12g, Fat: 10g, Fiber: 5g

Ingredients

- 200g snap peas, ends trimmed
- 1 tbsp sesame oil
- 1 tbsp sesame seeds
- Salt to taste

Directions

1. Preheat your oven to 375F. Toss the snap peas with sesame oil and salt.
2. To prepare the snap peas, spread them on a baking sheet and roast them for approximately 15 minutes until they become tender and slightly crispy. Sprinkle with sesame seeds before serving.

BEETROOT AND ORANGE SALAD

Prep time
10 Min

Cook Time
0 Min

Servings
1

Nutrition Information

Calories: 240, Protein: 4g,
Carbs: 30g, Fat: 12g, Fiber: 6g

Ingredients

- 1 medium beetroot, cooked and sliced
- 1 orange, peeled and segmented
- 2 cups mixed salad greens
- 1 tbsp olive oil
- 1 tbsp balsamic vinegar
- Salt and pepper to taste

Directions

1. Combine the beetroot, orange segments, and salad greens in a bowl.

Before serving:

2. Sprinkle the dish with olive oil and balsamic vinegar.
3. Season it with salt & pepper.
4. Toss everything together to coat evenly.

MOROCCAN SPICED ROASTED CARROTS

 Prep time
10 Min

 Cook Time
20 Min

 Servings
1

Nutrition Information

Calories: 160, Protein: 2g,
Carbs: 20g, Fat: 8g, Fiber: 6g

Ingredients

- 200g carrots, peeled and sliced
- 1 tbsp olive oil
- 1/2 tsp ground cumin
- 1/2 tsp ground coriander
- Salt and pepper to taste

Directions

1. Preheat your oven to 400F. Toss the carrots with olive oil, cumin, coriander, salt, and pepper.
2. Lay the carrots on an aluminum foil and roast for about 20 mins or tender and slightly caramelized.

TOMATO, CUCUMBER, AND RED ONION SALAD

 Prep time
10 Min

 Cook Time
0 Min

 Servings
1

Nutrition Information

Calories: 180, Protein: 3g,
Carbs: 14g, Fat: 14g, Fiber: 3g

Ingredients

- 1 large tomato, chopped
- 1/2 cucumber, chopped
- 1/4 red onion, thinly sliced
- 2 tbsp chopped fresh parsley
- 1 tbsp olive oil
- 1 tbsp lemon juice
- Salt and pepper to taste

Directions

1. Combine the tomato, cucumber, red onion, and parsley in a bowl.
2. Before serving, add a drizzle of oil and juice of lime, season with salt & pepper, and toss thoroughly.

GRILLED ZUCCHINI WITH LEMON SALT

 Prep time
10 Min

 Cook Time
10 Min

 Servings
1

Nutrition Information

Calories: 140, Protein: 3g,
Carbs: 6g, Fat: 12g, Fiber: 2g

Ingredients

- 1 medium zucchini, sliced lengthwise
- 1 tbsp olive oil
- Zest of 1 lemon
- 1/2 tsp coarse salt

Directions

1. Set your grill or grill pan over moderate heat. Brush the zucchini slices with olive oil.
2. For soft zucchini with grill marks, cook for 5 minutes per side.
3. Combine the lemon zest and coarse salt, and sprinkle over the grilled zucchini before serving.

STEAMED CORN ON THE COB WITH CHILI BUTTER

 Prep time
5 Min

 Cook Time
10 Min

 Servings
1

Nutrition Information

Calories: 190, Protein: 4g,
Carbs: 19g, Fat: 12g, Fiber: 2g

Ingredients

- 1 ear of corn
- 1 tbsp butter, softened
- 1/4 tsp chili powder
- Salt to taste

Directions

1. Steam the corn until it is tender, about 10 minutes.
2. Combine the butter, chili powder, and salt, and spread on the hot corn before serving.

WARM SPINACH SALAD WITH ROASTED MUSHROOMS

 Prep time
10 Min

 Cook Time
20 Min

 Servings
1

Nutrition Information

Calories: 190, Protein: 7g,
Carbs: 12g, Fat: 14g, Fiber: 4g

Ingredients

- 1 cup fresh spinach
- 200g assorted mushrooms, sliced
- 1 tbsp olive oil
- 1 tbsp balsamic vinegar
- Salt and pepper to taste

Directions

1. Preheat your oven to 400F. Coat the mushrooms evenly with olive oil, then season with salt and pepper.
2. Lay the mushrooms on an aluminum foil, and roast for about 20 minutes or until tender and slightly crispy.
3. Toss the hot mushrooms with the spinach and balsamic vinegar before serving. The heat from the mushrooms will wilt the spinach slightly.

CAPRESE SALAD WITH BALSAMIC REDUCTION

 Prep time
10 Min

 Cook Time
10 Min

 Servings
1

Nutrition Information

Calories: 350, Protein: 12g
Carbs: 12g, Fat: 26g, Fiber: 2g

Ingredients

- 1 large ripe tomato, sliced
- 60g fresh mozzarella cheese, sliced
- 6 fresh basil leaves
- 1 tbsp olive oil
- 1/4 cup balsamic vinegar

Directions

1. Arrange the tomato, mozzarella, and basil on a plate, alternating and overlapping them.
2. Drizzle with olive oil. Prepare the balsamic vinegar in a small saucepan over moderate heat until reduced by half, about 10 minutes, then drizzle over the salad before serving.

ROASTED SWEET POTATO WITH HONEY AND CINNAMON

 Prep time
10 Min

 Cook Time
25 Min

 Servings
1

Nutrition Information

Calories: 260, Protein: 2g,
Carbs: 46g, Fat: 7g, Fiber: 6g

Ingredients

- 1 medium sweet potato, cubed
- 1 tbsp olive oil
- 1 tbsp honey
- 1/2 tsp ground cinnamon
- Salt to taste

Directions

1. Preheat your oven to 400F. Toss the sweet potato with olive oil, honey, cinnamon, and salt.
2. Spread the sweet potato on Parchment paper and roast for about 25 minutes or until tender and caramelized.

ASIAN SLAW WITH SESAME GINGER DRESSING

 Prep time
15 Min

 Cook Time
0 Min

 Servings
1

Nutrition Information

Calories: 180, Protein: 3g,
Carbs: 10g, Fat: 14g, Fiber: 4g

Ingredients

- 2 cups shredded cabbage mix (red and green cabbage, carrots)
- 1 tbsp sesame oil
- 1 tbsp rice vinegar
- 1/2 tsp grated ginger
- 1/2 tsp sesame seeds
- Salt to taste

Directions

1. Combine the shredded cabbage mix with sesame oil, rice vinegar, grated ginger, and salt in a bowl. Toss well to combine.
2. Sprinkle with sesame seeds before serving.

GRILLED EGGPLANT WITH GARLIC YOGURT SAUCE

Prep time
10 Min

Cook Time
10 Min

Servings
1

Nutrition Information

Calories: 230, Protein: 7g,
Carbs: 20g, Fat: 14g, Fiber: 8g

Ingredients

- 1 medium eggplant, sliced into rounds
- 1 tbsp olive oil
- Salt and pepper to taste
- 1/4 cup plain Greek yogurt
- 1 clove garlic, minced

Directions

1. Prepare the grill or griddle pan by heating it to medium heat. The grill or pan should be heated to medium temperatures before use. Season the eggplant slices with salt & pepper and brush them with olive oil.
2. Turn the eggplant over and grill it for another 5 minutes or until grill marks emerge and it is soft.
3. Combine the Greek yogurt and minced garlic, and drizzle over the grilled eggplant before serving.

KALE SALAD WITH LEMON VINAIGRETTE

Prep time
15 Min

Cook Time
0 Min

Servings
1

Nutrition Information

Calories: 150, Protein: 5g,
Carbs: 10g, Fat: 10g, Fiber: 3g

Ingredients

- 2 cups kale, stems removed and leaves torn
- 1 tbsp olive oil
- 1 tbsp lemon juice
- Salt and pepper to taste
- 1 tbsp grated Parmesan cheese

Directions

1. Massage the kale in a large bowl with olive oil, lime juice, salt & pepper until the leaves soften and wilt.
2. Sprinkle with grated Parmesan cheese before serving.

7 DAYS MEAL PLAN

Day	Breakfast	Lunch	Dinner	Total Calories	Total Protein
Day 1	Egg and Spinach Breakfast Scramble Pg # 12	Grilled Chicken Caesar Salad Pg # 33	Grilled Lamb Chops with Mint Chimichurri Pg # 93	1230 Kcal	102g
Day 2	Chicken Sausage and Bell Pepper Omelette Pg # 13	Shrimp and Avocado Salad Pg # 38	Tofu and Broccoli Stir-Fry Pg # 91	1120 Kcal	112g
Day 3	Chickpea Pancakes with Smoked Salmon Pg # 17	Beef and Broccoli Stir-Fry Pg # 39	Chicken with Couscous Pg # 88	1150 Kcal	104
Day4	Avocado Toast with Boiled Eggs Pg # 19	Spicy Noodles with Lean Beef, Scallions & Bok Choy Pg # 43	Paella with Seafood and Chicken Pg # 85	1370 Kcal	101g
Day 5	Vegan Tofu and Vegetable Frittata Pg # 23	Seared Tuna Steak with Avocado and Mango Salsa Pg # 45	Osso Buco with Gremolata Pg # 82	1280 Kcal	105g
Day 6	Baked Oatmeal with Berries and Cottage Cheese Pg # 25	Lamb Tagine with Chickpeas and Apricots Pg # 48	Black Pepper Beef Stir-fry Pg # 80	1250 Kcal	100g
Day 7	Three-Minute Egg White Oatmeal Pg # 30	Sesame Chicken with Green Beans Pg # 51	Miso Glazed Salmon Pg # 78	1030 Kcal	100g

CONCLUSION

Incorporating a sufficient amount of protein into your daily diet is essential for supporting overall health, maintaining muscle mass, and achieving your fitness goals. With this collection of 120 high-protein recipes, we have provided you with a diverse range of options to help you meet your protein needs while enjoying delicious and nutritious meals.

Throughout this book, we have focused on incorporating a variety of protein sources such as chicken, seafood, lean beef, tofu, eggs, and more. By diversifying your protein intake, you can not only meet your daily protein requirements but also enjoy a wide range of flavors and nutritional benefits.

Each recipe is carefully crafted to provide a balance of macronutrients, including carbohydrates, fats, and fiber, and is designed to fit within the calorie range of 300 to 550 calories. This ensures that you can enjoy satisfying meals without compromising your caloric intake or nutritional goals.

We understand that planning and preparing meals can be time-consuming, which is why we have included a 7-day meal prep example to help you streamline your meal planning process. This meal prep guide offers a practical and convenient approach to incorporating high-protein recipes into your daily routine, saving you time and effort while ensuring you meet your protein goals.

By utilizing the recipes, meal planning tips, and high-protein sources provided in this book, you can embark on a culinary journey that combines taste and nutrition. Whether you're looking to build muscle, lose weight, or simply improve

your overall well-being, this collection of recipes will empower you to create flavorful and protein-rich meals that support your health and fitness goals.

We hope this book serves as a valuable resource in your journey towards a protein-rich lifestyle. Remember to listen to your body, adjust the recipes to your taste preferences, and experiment with different ingredients and cooking methods. Enjoy the process of nourishing your body with these protein-packed recipes and experience the benefits of a well-balanced and high-protein diet.

Here's to delicious meals, optimal health, and reaching your protein goals!

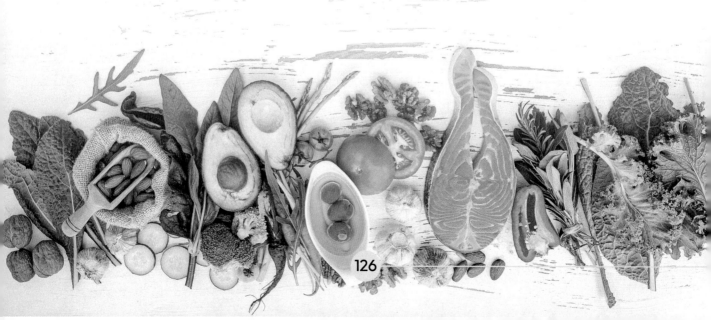

Made in the USA
Middletown, DE
24 October 2024